A SURVEY OF
LIE GROUPS AND LIE ALGEBRAS
WITH APPLICATIONS AND
COMPUTATIONAL METHODS

A SURVEY
OF
LIE GROUPS AND LIE ALGEBRAS
WITH
APPLICATIONS AND COMPUTATIONAL
METHODS

JOHAN G. F. BELINFANTE
Carnegie-Mellon University, Pittsburgh

BERNARD KOLMAN
Drexel University, Philadelphia

SOCIETY FOR INDUSTRIAL AND APPLIED MATHEMATICS
Philadelphia

The work of Bernard Kolman was supported in part by the Air Force Office of Scientific Research, Air Force Systems Command, United States Air Force, under AFOSR Grant 69-1797.

Society for Industrial and Applied Mathematics
33 South 17th Street, Philadelphia, Pennsylvania 19103

Library of Congress Catalogue Card Number: 72-77081

TABLE OF CONTENTS

Chapter 3. CONSTRUCTIVE METHODS   91

PREFACE

Applications of the theory of Lie groups, Lie algebras and their representations are many and varied. This is a rapidly growing field through which one can bring to bear many powerful methods of modern mathematics.

In the contemporary literature on applied Lie theory, one often encounters background material available only in research articles and advanced treatises. This monograph introduces the modern concepts and methods of Lie theory used in current applications in a form accessible to the non-specialist by keeping the mathematical prerequisites to a minimum. This objective has forced us to concentrate on the presentation of results while omitting most of the proofs. We have compensated for this omission by including many references to the original literature.

Our treatment is directed primarily toward the reader who wants a broad view of the subject, rather than elaborate information about technical details. Much of the material in this monograph has been used by the authors in various courses given to applied mathematicians, physicists and engineers.

The material covered in this monograph is a considerably updated, revised and expanded version of material originally published as a series of three survey papers in the *SIAM Review* [28], [29], [30], the first two of which were written in collaboration with Harvey A. Smith. It also includes material on computational methods using electronic digital computers which was developed by the authors in collaboration respectively with Vishnu K. Agrawala and Robert E. Beck.

Chapter 1, following the Introduction, deals with the basic properties of Lie groups and Lie algebras, Chapter 2 covers representation theory, and Chapter 3, on constructive methods, presents the computational aspects of the subject.

We have resisted the constant temptation to cast Lie theory in its most general and abstract form. This approach seems to us to be a good way of breaking down the barriers erected by excessive specialization in this area. On the other hand, we have not neglected recent advances in the representation theory of Lie algebras, since these are needed for many of the applications. The material on applications, which is spread throughout the book, has been included not only for its own sake, but also to provide motivation and to illustrate various points in the Lie theory itself. Extensive simplifications and generalizations of the classical representation theory have recently been made by pure mathematicians, and we hope that this monograph will help to diffuse some of these important new mathematical ideas.

To help the reader locate the various definitions, these have been set in italic type, and are listed in the Index. In the References, all authors appear in alphabetical order, and all titles in foreign languages have been translated into English.

JOHAN G. F. BELINFANTE
BERNARD KOLMAN

ACKNOWLEDGMENTS

We express our thanks to Harvey A. Smith who collaborated with us on the first two *SIAM Review* papers which served as a nucleus for this monograph; to Vishnu K. Agrawala and to Robert E. Beck who collaborated with us on the computer approaches to representation theory which are described in this book; to P. Cartier for two discussions on the terminology concerning layers and levels and on computing aspects of representation theory; and to T. Shimpuku, who furnished us with valuable information on Clifford algebras. We are grateful to many readers of the *SIAM Review* survey papers for numerous valuable suggestions, some of which have been incorporated in the present work. Robert E. Beck and Roger W. Brockett deserve our thanks for reading the manuscript and offering many suggestions and criticisms.

We are grateful to Miss Susan R. Gershuni who typed the entire manuscript and its revisions and to our wives, Irene and Lillie, who helped with the preparation of the manuscript. We thank the entire staff of SIAM for their interest, encouragement and cooperation in this project.

A SURVEY OF
LIE GROUPS AND LIE ALGEBRAS
WITH APPLICATIONS AND
COMPUTATIONAL METHODS

INTRODUCTION

The theory of Lie groups and Lie algebras is an area of mathematics in which we can see a harmonious interaction between the methods of classical analysis and modern algebra. This theory, a direct outgrowth of a central problem in the calculus, has today become a synthesis of many separate disciplines, each of which has left its own mark.

The theory of Lie groups was developed by the Norwegian mathematician Sophus Lie in the late nineteenth century in connection with his work on systems of differential equations. Lie groups arise in the study of solutions of differential equations just as finite groups arise in the study of algebraic equations. The possibility of solving many differential equations which arise in practical problems can often be traced to some geometrical or other symmetry property of the problem. Indeed, Lie groups play a fundamental role in many parts of geometry itself, and have contributed significantly to the development of that subject. Thus, for many years Lie theory has been found useful in such areas of pure mathematics as the differential geometry of symmetric spaces. Conversely, geometrical methods have played a dominant role in the structure theory of Lie groups and Lie algebras.

In our exposition of this structure theory, we focus on the classification of real and complex semisimple Lie algebras. We found this to be an excellent place to introduce and apply many of the tools of classical linear algebra and vector space theory, as well as the modern theory of modules.

The importance of Lie algebras and Lie groups for applied mathematics and for physics has also become increasingly evident in recent years. In applied mathematics, Lie theory remains a powerful tool for studying differential equations, special functions and perturbation theory. Lie theory often enters into physics either through the presence of exact kinematical symmetries or through the use of idealized dynamical models having greater symmetry than is present in the real world. These exact kinematical symmetries include rotational, translational and Galilean or Lorentz invariance, as well as symmetries arising from the use of canonical formalism in both classical and quantum mechanics. Broken symmetries arising from approximate models are encountered in atomic and nuclear spectroscopy, and in elementary particle physics.

3

Since much of the applied literature nowadays presumes a quite detailed familiarity with the methods of representation theory, we include a leisurely treatment of this crucial aspect of the subject. We discuss here the concepts of representations and modules, the standard module operations, and the classification of the finite-dimensional modules over semisimple Lie algebras. We also discuss in detail various computational methods, including the explicit construction of the irreducible modules, which are needed for calculating Clebsch–Gordan and Racah coefficients.

The study of the constructive aspects of Lie module theory has become practical recently through the use of computers. Computers provide a valuable new research tool in Lie theory, which makes it possible to test various theoretical conjectures about the representations of Lie algebras. We believe this area of Lie theory will continue to grow rapidly for some time to come. Our discussion of the use of computers, with the resulting emphasis on constructive methods, is just one of the ways we have kept Lie theory from becoming too abstract. In addition, we have throughout this volume presented diverse applications to topics in mathematics and physics to illustrate various points of Lie theory. In our selection of such topics we have tried to indicate a few of the many interesting directions in which applied research on the Lie theory has been carried out.

However, our primary aim has always been to use applications only to provide some motivation for discussing various aspects of Lie theory itself. We do not claim to have given a comprehensive treatment of even the major applications. Lie theory finds application not only in elementary particle physics and nuclear physics, but also in such diverse fields as continuum mechanics, solid-state physics, cosmology and control theory. Much was left out to keep the discussion within manageable dimensions, and the reader will realize that to pursue the applications seriously, one must go beyond the material presented here. Hopefully the bibliography will prove to be useful as a guide for collateral reading, but it is necessarily incomplete and we must apologize to those authors whose work has been left out.

LIE GROUPS AND LIE ALGEBRAS

1.1 THE GENERAL LINEAR GROUP

Since many of the central ideas of Lie theory arose in the study of geometry and linear algebra, it is fitting to begin with a review of some topics in vector space theory so that we can begin to talk about some of the essential tools, such as the Lie algebra and tensor algebra constructions. It is also instructive to examine the classical linear Lie groups before getting involved with the rather technical general definition of a Lie group.

We recall that a *linear mapping* $\alpha: V_1 \to V_2$ from a vector space V_1 into a vector space V_2 is a mapping which preserves vector addition and scalar multiplication:

$$\alpha(x + y) = \alpha(x) + \alpha(y), \qquad \text{where } x, y \in V_1,$$

and

$$\alpha(\lambda x) = \lambda \alpha(x),$$
$$\text{where } x \in V_1 \quad \text{and} \quad \lambda \text{ is a scalar}.$$

In particular, a *linear operator* on a vector space V is a linear mapping from V into itself. A linear operator has an inverse if and only if it is both one-to-one and onto as a mapping. The set of all invertible linear operators on a vector space V is a group called the *general linear group* on V.

In the general linear group we take the group operation to be the ordinary composition of linear operators. A linear operator on a finite-dimensional vector space is invertible if and only if its determinant is nonzero. The general linear group on a finite-dimensional vector space consists therefore of all linear operators with nonzero determinants. The set of all linear operators with determinant one forms a subgroup called the *special linear group* on V.

If we introduce a basis into the vector space, each linear operator can be represented by a matrix and we can talk in terms of *matrix groups*. Thus, the *matrix* of a linear operator α with respect to a basis $e_1, \cdots, e_n$ for V is the array of scalars $[\alpha^i{}_j]$ determined by

$$\alpha e_j = \sum_{i=1}^{n} \alpha^i{}_j e_i.$$

The general and special linear groups may then be regarded as groups of matrices, the group operation being matrix multiplication. These groups of

5

matrices can be defined for any field of scalars such as, for instance, the real number field $\mathbb{R}$ or the complex number field $\mathbb{C}$. Thus, in particular we obtain the group of all nonsingular complex $n \times n$ matrices, called the *complex general linear group GL(n, $\mathbb{C}$)*.

The *real general linear group GL(n, $\mathbb{R}$)*, consisting of all real nonsingular $n \times n$ matrices, may be regarded as a subgroup of the complex general linear group. The *complex special linear group SL(n, $\mathbb{C}$)* is the subgroup of $GL(n, \mathbb{C})$ consisting of matrices with determinant one. The intersection of these two subgroups is the *real special linear group*,

$$SL(n, \mathbb{R}) = SL(n, \mathbb{C}) \cap GL(n, \mathbb{R}).$$

The special linear groups are sometimes also called *unimodular groups*. The reader should be warned however that in abstract harmonic analysis the same term, unimodular group, is used in a completely different sense [152].

1.2   ORTHOGONAL AND UNITARY GROUPS

Other important subgroups of the general linear group $GL(n, \mathbb{C})$ are familiar from elementary matrix theory. These include the group of complex orthogonal matrices $O(n, \mathbb{C})$ and the group of unitary matrices $U(n)$. We recall that a matrix is *orthogonal* if its transpose is its inverse, while a matrix is *unitary* if its transposed complex conjugate is its inverse. We obtain "special" versions of these groups by taking their intersections with the complex special linear group. The *special complex orthogonal group* is

$$SO(n, \mathbb{C}) = O(n, \mathbb{C}) \cap SL(n, \mathbb{C}).$$

The *special unitary group* is

$$SU(n) = U(n) \cap SL(n, \mathbb{C}).$$

The determinant of an orthogonal matrix can only be $+1$ or -1. This is because the determinant of the transpose of a matrix is the same as that of the matrix, while the determinant of the inverse matrix is the reciprocal of its determinant. Orthogonal matrices are classified as *proper* or *improper*, depending upon whether their determinants are $+1$ or -1. Thus we may also describe the special orthogonal group as the group of all proper orthogonal matrices.

By considering further intersections of the above groups with the real general linear group, we obtain some groups which are important in Euclidean geometry. The *real orthogonal group* is defined as

$$O(n, \mathbb{R}) = O(n, \mathbb{C}) \cap GL(n, \mathbb{R})$$
$$= U(n) \cap GL(n, \mathbb{R})$$
$$= U(n) \cap O(n, \mathbb{C}).$$

The real orthogonal group may be considered as the group of all rigid motions which leave a given point fixed. The *rotation group* is the special or proper real orthogonal group,

$$SO(n, \mathbb{R}) = O(n, \mathbb{R}) \cap SL(n, \mathbb{C}).$$

The geometrical interpretation of the distinction between proper and improper orthogonal matrices can be studied explicitly for low dimension. For $n = 2$, every improper orthogonal matrix can be interpreted geometrically as a reflection, but this is not the case for $n = 3$. For example, the *parity* or *inversion operation*, represented by the negative of the unit matrix, is not a mirror reflection for $n = 3$, but it is nevertheless improper. In general the parity operation behaves differently in even and odd dimension, being a rotation for even n and improper only for odd n. Thus, it is not too surprising that the relation between the groups $O(n, \mathbb{R})$ and $SO(n, \mathbb{R})$ is somewhat different for even and odd n. For odd n, the group $O(n, \mathbb{R})$ is simply the direct product of $SO(n, \mathbb{R})$ with the group Z_2 consisting of ± 1. This is not true for even n as can be seen in the case $n = 2$. Indeed, since $SO(2, \mathbb{R})$ and Z_2 are Abelian, so is their direct product, while the group $O(2, \mathbb{R})$ is non-Abelian. Nevertheless, the general relation between $O(n, \mathbb{R})$ and $SO(n, \mathbb{R})$ is rather simple and can be described formally in terms of quotient groups.

The mapping which assigns to each matrix its determinant provides a homomorphism from the group $O(n, \mathbb{R})$ onto the finite group Z_2. The kernel of this homomorphism is just the rotation group $SO(n, \mathbb{R})$, so that the rotation group is a normal subgroup of $O(n, \mathbb{R})$. Hence, by the fundamental homomorphism theorem, the quotient group of $O(n, \mathbb{R})$ with respect to $SO(n, \mathbb{R})$ is isomorphic to Z_2.

1.3 GROUPS IN GEOMETRY

Matrix Lie groups also arise in various types of non-Euclidean geometry, and are sometimes encountered in applications. An important example is the *Lorentz group*, which is an indefinite-metric version of the orthogonal group for the geometry of space-time in the special theory of relativity. Another group, the *symplectic group*, plays an important role in the geometry of phase space in classical mechanics. To obtain a deeper understanding of the geometrical significance of the orthogonal and symplectic groups, we turn to some elementary notions from the theory of bilinear forms [134].

A *bilinear form* on a vector space V over a field $\mathbb{F}$ is a function which assigns to each ordered pair of vectors x and y in V a scalar $(x, y) \in \mathbb{F}$, and which satisfies the following properties for any scalars α and β and any vectors x, y and z in V:

$$(\alpha x + \beta y, z) = \alpha(x, z) + \beta(y, z),$$
$$(x, \alpha y + \beta z) = \alpha(x, y) + \beta(x, z).$$

A bilinear form (x, y) can be completely described by its matrix $\beta_{ij} = (e_i, e_j)$ with respect to any basis $e_1, \cdots, e_n$. Indeed, if we are given this matrix, then for any vectors

$$x = \sum_i \xi^i e_i \quad \text{and} \quad y = \sum_j \eta^j e_j,$$

we can compute

$$(x, y) = \sum_{i,j} \beta_{ij} \xi^i \eta^j.$$

A bilinear form (x, y) is *symmetric* if $(x, y) = (y, x)$ for all x and y in V. If (x, y) is a symmetric bilinear form, then its matrix β is equal to its own transpose. Similarly, we say that a bilinear form (x, y) is *antisymmetric* if $(x, y) = -(y, x)$ for all x and y in V, and in this case β is equal to the negative of its transpose. A familiar example of a symmetric bilinear form is, of course, the inner product in Euclidean vector geometry. In Riemannian geometry, the metric tensor and the curvature tensor are both examples of symmetric bilinear forms.

Symmetric bilinear forms also occur naturally in the study of linear operators in vector spaces of finite dimension. We may define such a bilinear form by using the trace operation $\mathrm{Tr}_V(\ )$ for linear operators on a vector space V. If we introduce a basis, the *trace* of a linear operator is the sum of its diagonal matrix elements

$$\mathrm{Tr}_V(\alpha) = \sum_i \alpha^i{}_i.$$

Since the trace of an operator is also equal to the sum of its eigenvalues, counting multiple roots of the characteristic equation, it does not matter which basis we use here. The set $\mathrm{lin}_\mathbb{F}(V)$ of all linear operators on an n-dimensional vector space V over a field $\mathbb{F}$ is itself an n^2-dimensional vector space over $\mathbb{F}$. Then $\mathrm{Tr}_V(\alpha\beta)$ defines a bilinear form on the vector space $\mathrm{lin}_\mathbb{F}(V)$. This type of symmetric bilinear form is important in the study of the structure of Lie groups and Lie algebras.

The introduction of a symmetric or antisymmetric bilinear form in a vector space leads naturally to the idea of orthogonality of vectors. Vectors x and y in V are said to be *orthogonal* if $(x, y) = 0$. Much of the theory of symmetric bilinear forms also applies to antisymmetric bilinear forms, and we may discuss the two cases simultaneously.

For a symmetric or antisymmetric bilinear form, the orthogonality of vectors is a symmetric relation; if x is orthogonal to y, then y is also orthogonal to x. A nonzero vector x is said to be *isotropic*, or a *null vector*, if it is orthogonal to itself, $(x, x) = 0$, and *anisotropic* if $(x, x) \neq 0$. Isotropic vectors are of course not present in Euclidean geometry, but they often occur in more general situations. In special relativity theory, isotropic vectors are called *light-like* because light rays travel in straight lines along the directions of such vectors. For symmetric bilinear forms over the complex number field, isotropic vectors occur in any vector space having dimension ≥ 2. If we are dealing with antisymmetric bilinear forms over the real or complex number field, then every vector is isotropic.

For the discussion of the orthogonal and symplectic groups, we shall restrict our attention to nonsingular bilinear forms. A bilinear form is *nonsingular* if the only vector orthogonal to every other vector is zero, that is, if $(x, y) = 0$ for all y in V implies that $x = 0$. The bilinear form (x, y) is nonsingular if and only if its matrix β is invertible, which means that $\det \beta \neq 0$. It should be noted that whether or not a bilinear form is nonsingular, its restriction to a subspace need not be nonsingular. Thus the notion of nonsingularity also leads to a classification of the subspaces of a vector space, and this is often useful in the structure theory of vector spaces equipped with bilinear forms.

An *orthogonal linear operator* α with respect to a nonsingular symmetric bilinear form is a linear operator for which

$$(\alpha x, \alpha y) = (x, y)$$

holds for all x and y in V. If x belongs to the kernel (null space) of an orthogonal linear operator α, then we have $\alpha x = 0$, and hence for all y we find $(x, y) = (\alpha x, \alpha y) = 0$. If the bilinear form is nonsingular, then $x = 0$ and α is one-to-one, and if V is finite-dimensional, this further implies that α is invertible. Thus the set of orthogonal linear operators in this case forms a group, which we call the *orthogonal group* with respect to the given symmetric bilinear form.

We obtain the matrix groups mentioned earlier by introducing bases for vector spaces equipped with nonsingular bilinear forms. The matrix β describing the bilinear form depends on the choice of the basis $e_1, \cdots, e_n$. If β' is the matrix of this same bilinear form with respect to another basis $e'_1, \cdots, e'_n$, where $e'_i = \sum_j \sigma^j{}_i e_j$, then β' is related to β by the *congruence transformation*

$$\beta'_{ij} = \sum_{k,l} \beta_{kl} \sigma^k{}_i \sigma^l{}_j.$$

We can make use of such congruence transformations to bring the matrix β to a canonical form. It is a standard result of matrix theory that we can choose the matrix σ so that β' is a diagonal matrix [191]. The exact form of the diagonal matrix depends on whether we are considering bilinear forms over the real or complex number fields.

In the complex case, when $\det \beta \neq 0$, we can arrange it so that β' is the identity matrix. Thus for a nonsingular symmetric bilinear form over the complex number field, we can always find an orthonormal basis for V. A basis $e_1, \cdots, e_n$ is said to be *orthonormal* if

$$(e_i, e_j) = \delta_{ij},$$

where the *Kronecker delta* δ_{ij} is equal to 1 if $i = j$ and 0 if $i \neq j$. The matrix of an orthogonal linear operator with respect to an orthonormal basis satisfies the condition that its inverse is its transpose. Therefore, we obtain just one orthogonal group for each dimension in the complex case, namely the group $O(n, \mathbb{C})$.

In the real case, if $\det \beta \neq 0$, we can find a matrix σ so that β' is diagonal and its diagonal elements are ± 1. The *signature* (p, q), where p and q are the numbers of $+1$'s and -1's respectively on the diagonal, is an invariant of the real symmetric bilinear form. In the special case where $p = n$ and $q = 0$, the real symmetric bilinear form is said to be *positive definite* because $(x, x) > 0$ for all $x \neq 0$, and we obtain the ordinary real orthogonal group $O(n, \mathbb{R})$. In the general case, the group $O(p, q; \mathbb{R})$ which we obtain may be described as an *orthogonal group with an indefinite metric* of signature (p, q) in a space of dimension $n = p + q$. An example of this is the *Lorentz group* $O(3, 1; \mathbb{R})$, which is just the orthogonal group of the Minkowski space-time $\mathbb{R}^4$ $(+ + + -)$.

The definition of the symplectic groups is somewhat similar to that of the orthogonal groups. Just as the orthogonal groups consist of linear operators which leave invariant a symmetric nonsingular bilinear form, the *symplectic groups* consist of linear operators which leave invariant an antisymmetric nonsingular bilinear form. A *symplectic linear operator* α is an operator satisfying

$$(\alpha x, \alpha y) = (x, y)$$

for an antisymmetric nonsingular bilinear form. Nonsingular antisymmetric bilinear forms can only occur in vector spaces V which have even dimension, $\dim V = 2n$. In any such space we can find a *hyperbolic basis* $e_{\pm 1}, \cdots, e_{\pm n}$ such that

$$(e_i, e_j) = (e_{-i}, e_{-j}) = 0,$$

$$(e_i, e_{-j}) = \delta_{ij}$$

for all $i, j = 1, \cdots, n$.

To describe the matrices of symplectic linear operators with respect to such a basis, we introduce the $2n \times 2n$ matrix

$$J = \begin{bmatrix} 0 & 1 \\ -1 & 0 \end{bmatrix},$$

where 1 denotes the $n \times n$ identity matrix. The matrix group $Sp(n, \mathbb{C})$ is then the set of all complex $2n \times 2n$ matrices A which satisfy

$$A^T J A = J,$$

where A^T denotes the transpose of the matrix A. Closely related to this *complex symplectic group* $Sp(n, \mathbb{C})$ are some other matrix groups obtained by taking intersections. Since we can find hyperbolic bases in both real and complex vector spaces, there is also only one real symplectic group. This *real symplectic group* is the intersection

$$Sp(n, \mathbb{R}) = Sp(n, \mathbb{C}) \cap GL(2n, \mathbb{R}).$$

We may also mention here the *unitary symplectic group,*

$$Sp(n) = Sp(n, \mathbb{C}) \cap U(2n).$$

Taking intersections with $SL(n, \mathbb{C})$ gives nothing new since every symplectic linear operator already has determinant one [10]. The symplectic groups have been applied to various problems in nuclear physics [121]. There are many other matrix groups, and more extensive catalogues of them can be found in the literature [120].

1.4 THE EXPONENTIAL MAPPING

The classical matrix groups which have been discussed so far are all defined by imposing various algebraic conditions on the matrices belonging to the group. When these conditions are written out in terms of the matrix elements, we obtain complicated nonlinear equations to solve. It is remarkable that in each case these nonlinear conditions can be replaced by an equivalent set of linear conditions. This is in fact the essential idea behind the passage from Lie groups to Lie algebras. The actual relation between Lie groups and Lie algebras can be described in several different ways. To expedite matters, we shall consider here the fastest way to get to the Lie algebra by using the concept of matrix exponentiation. Although this method does not work for all Lie groups, it is sufficient for the classical matrix groups.

For any square matrix A, we define $\exp(A)$ by the power series

$$I + A + A^2/2! + \cdots + A^n/n! + \cdots,$$

where I is the identity matrix, and each matrix element converges absolutely. Thus, for example, we have $\exp(0) = I$. From the inverse function theorem, it is easily seen that every matrix in some neighborhood of the identity in $GL(n, \mathbb{C})$ can be expressed as $\exp(A)$ for some $n \times n$ complex matrix A. For $GL(n, \mathbb{R})$, we can restrict the matrix A to be real. In the case of $GL(n, \mathbb{R})$, the exponential map does not yield the whole group, as can be seen by considering the case where $n = 1$. The group $GL(1, \mathbb{R})$ is the real line with the origin removed, while the image of the exponential map is only the positive real axis. This is the price that must be paid for using the exponential map; that is, we may sometimes lose the global structure of the group. The local structure however is completely preserved.

To assure that the matrix $\exp(A)$ will belong to a given one of the classical matrix Lie groups we have discussed, we require the matrix A to satisfy a suitable linear condition. For the special linear groups, we can replace the nonlinear condition on $\exp(A)$ involving the determinant by a linear condition on A involving the trace. If λ is an eigenvalue of A, then $\exp(\lambda)$ is an eigenvalue of $\exp(A)$ with the same eigenspace. The determinant of $\exp(A)$, being the product of its eigenvalues, is equal to $\exp(\text{Tr}(A))$ since the trace $\text{Tr}(A)$ is the sum of the eigenvalues of A. Hence the determinant of $\exp(A)$ is one if and only if the trace of A is zero.

We may also use the exponential map to get linear conditions in the case of the orthogonal, unitary and symplectic groups. The transpose of the exponential of a matrix is the exponential of its transpose, and the inverse of the exponential of a matrix is the exponential of its negative. Hence, a sufficient condition for exp (A) to be orthogonal is that A be antisymmetric. Similarly, the complex conjugate of exp (A) is the exponential of the complex conjugate of A. Hence, exp (A) is unitary when A is equal to the negative of its transposed complex conjugate. Such a matrix is called *anti-Hermitian*. Finally, we note that exp (A) is symplectic if A satisfies $A^T J + J A = 0$, which is again a linear condition.

In summary, the exponential mapping allows us to replace the classical matrix Lie groups by sets of matrices which satisfy various linear conditions. Such sets of matrices are of course closed under taking arbitrary real linear combinations, and we may view these sets as vector spaces. These sets of matrices are not closed under ordinary matrix multiplication. However, if A and B are matrices which are, respectively, antisymmetric, anti-Hermitian or traceless, then $AB - BA$ also has that property. Hence, the sets of matrices with which one has to deal are not only vector spaces, but are also closed under an additional operation, and one says that they form a Lie algebra. The study of these Lie algebras, as well as others just like them, forms the central core of the Lie theory.

1.5   LIE AND ASSOCIATIVE ALGEBRAS

Before studying the Lie algebras of the classical matrix groups in detail, it is useful to discuss Lie algebras in general from a slightly more formal viewpoint. In addition, we wish to discuss some relations existing between Lie algebras and associative algebras. In general, any vector space endowed with a bilinear vector multiplication is called a *nonassociative algebra* [207]. That is, a nonassociative algebra consists of a vector space V together with any bilinear mapping $V \times V \to V$. The product of two vectors x, y in V then is another vector xy in V. If the vector multiplication is associative, so that $(xy)z = x(yz)$, then we speak of an *associative algebra*. For example, the set $\lin_{\mathbb{F}} (V)$ of all linear operators on a vector space V over a field $\mathbb{F}$ is an associative algebra under the usual multiplication of linear operators. This same vector space $\lin_{\mathbb{F}} (V)$ also has another algebra structure defined on it by taking the product of linear operators α and β to be the *commutator* $\alpha\beta - \beta\alpha$. To distinguish this product from the usual product, we use a special square bracket notation $[\alpha, \beta]$ for it. The resulting algebra is a nonassociative algebra of a certain special type called a Lie algebra.

Abstractly, a *Lie algebra* L is a vector space equipped with a product $[x, y]$ satisfying certain axioms [73], [82], [83], [135], [228]. We shall continue to use the bracket notation for products when we deal with any Lie algebra. One of the axioms for a Lie algebra is that the product $[x, y]$ be *bilinear*, that is, linear in x and y separately. We also assume that the Lie product is *anti-commutative*,

$$[x, y] = -[y, x].$$

Finally we assume that the *Jacobi identity*

$$[x, [y, z]] + [y, [z, x]] + [z, [x, y]] = 0$$

holds for all vectors x, y, z in the Lie algebra. The Jacobi identity plays for Lie algebras the same role that the associative law plays for associative algebras. While we can define Lie algebras over any field, we shall in practice only consider Lie algebras over the real and complex fields.

Undoubtedly the most familiar abstract Lie algebra is the real three-dimensional vector space with the vector cross product as multiplication. Obviously the vector cross product Lie algebra can also be defined for a three-dimensional vector space over any field. Anticommutativity of the vector cross product is familiar, and the Jacobi identity for cross products can be verified by a direct computation, using

$$\mathbf{a} \times (\mathbf{b} \times \mathbf{c}) = (\mathbf{a} \cdot \mathbf{c})\mathbf{b} - (\mathbf{a} \cdot \mathbf{b})\mathbf{c}.$$

For $\lin_F (V)$ with the commutator multiplication it is likewise easy to verify directly that the Lie algebra axioms are satisfied. The procedure used to give $\lin_F (V)$ a Lie algebra structure can be extended to any associative algebra. A Lie product can be defined in any associative algebra by the commutator $[x, y] = xy - yx$, making it a Lie algebra. Here the anticommutativity axiom is clearly satisfied, and the reader can check that in this case the Jacobi identity for the commutator follows from the associative law for the ordinary product.

There is another and perhaps more revealing way in which Lie algebras arise in the study of algebras. A *derivation d* of a nonassociative algebra A is a linear operator on A satisfying the formal analogue of the Leibniz rule for differentiating a product,

$$d(xy) = (dx)y + x(dy),$$

for all elements x and y in A. If $p(x)$ is any polynomial in x, then the differential operator $p(x) \, d/dx$ is an example of a derivation of the algebra of polynomials in x. In fact, the concept of a derivation is just an abstraction of the idea of a first order differential operator. The set of all derivations on a nonassociative algebra A is clearly a subspace of the linear operator algebra $\lin_F (A)$. Although the product of derivations is in general not a derivation, the commutator $d_1 d_2 - d_2 d_1$ of two derivations is again a derivation. Thus the set of all derivations of a nonassociative algebra is a Lie algebra, which we call the *derivation algebra* of the given nonassociative algebra.

1.6 LIE GROUPS

The general theory of Lie groups seeks to unify and to extend the discussion of the various classical groups. The extension of the theory comes about by treating not only matrix groups, but other types of groups as well.

Basically, a Lie group is the structure which naturally results when analytic machinery is coupled with abstract group theory. Curvilinear coordinates, derivatives, and power series become available as tools for the study of the resulting structure. Technically, a Lie group is first of all required to be a *topological group*, that is, it must be possible to assign a topology under which the group operation and taking inverses are both continuous functions [129], [164], [192]. The general concept of a topological group already leads to a very rich theory in which some of the methods of calculus, especially integration theory, can be applied. To make use of the full power of all the methods of calculus, including differentiation, we must introduce an analytic structure as well as a topology. A proper discussion of the analytic structure of a Lie group requires the concept of an analytic manifold [38], [42], [54], [64].

Historically, the concept of an analytic manifold grew out of the theory of Riemann surfaces in complex variable theory [238]. The theory of differentiable and analytic manifolds has since become the basis for modern differential geometry [127], [230]. The idea of defining a Lie group in terms of analytic manifolds did not gain widespread acceptance until almost half a century after Lie's original work [163]. Moreover, it turned out that any connected real analytic manifold may always be analytically embedded in a Euclidean space, so that it appears after all that manifold theory is somewhat of a luxury [171]. Therefore, instead of using the intrinsic definition, we shall regard a *connected analytic manifold* more intuitively as a smooth surface in a Euclidean space of suitable dimensions. In general, an analytic manifold will consist of several pieces if it is not connected. About each point of the manifold there is required to be an open set with all points within this open set being located by a curvilinear coordinate system. It is also required that the assignment of coordinates to points be a continuous mapping with a continuous inverse. Such an open subset of a manifold is called a *coordinate neighborhood* or *coordinate patch*, and the coordinate system is said to give a *chart* of this neighborhood. To avoid singular points like the poles on a Mercator projection map, we use many charts, forming an *atlas* which covers the manifold, each point of the manifold belonging to at least one chart. In general, these charts may overlap somewhat so that two coordinate neighborhoods may have a point in common. Overlapping charts are required to be *analytically related*, meaning that for any common point, the coordinates in each system are analytic functions of those in the other. A function defined in Euclidean space $\mathbb{R}^n$ is *analytic* at a point if it can be expressed as a convergent Taylor series in some neighborhood of the point.

A *Lie group* is a group which is also an analytic manifold and for which the group operations are analytic functions. Because of the analytic structure, each element of the group is specified by some curvilinear coordinate system. The multiplication of elements of a Lie group is required to be analytic in terms of these coordinates. Thus if x and y are points of the group, and if $z = x \circ y$, where $\circ$ denotes the group operation, then we require that the coordinates of z be analytic functions of those of x and y. We need not separately postulate that the mapping $x \mapsto x^{-1}$ be analytic, because this actually follows from the analyticity of the multiplication [64]. The analyticity requirements in the definition of a Lie group can be weakened to differentiability requirements, since the latter imply the former in this case. As a matter of fact, it is possible to characterize Lie groups by even weaker conditions [170].

For completeness we should mention that the theory of Lie groups does not provide the only possible way of unifying the classical groups. The theory of algebraic groups is an alternative approach which has the advantage over the Lie theory in that the restriction to the real or complex number fields can be removed. Unfortunately, the theory becomes much more complicated when general fields are permitted, and this more general concept has not yet proved to be useful outside of pure mathematics.

1.7 LIE ALGEBRAS OF LIE GROUPS

The whole atlas of charts of a Lie group can be generated from the charts at the identity element. If U is a coordinate neighborhood of an element g, then the set $g^{-1}U$ obtained by letting g^{-1} act on all elements of U will contain a coordinate neighborhood of the identity element. By this procedure, every coordinate neighborhood can be transported back to the identity, and it suffices to study what happens close to the identity. For convenience, coordinates in a neighborhood of the identity will be chosen so that the coordinates of the identity are zero. If x is a member of the group, we denote its coordinates by x^i. If $x \circ y = z$, we have $z^i(x^1, \cdots, x^n, y^1, \cdots, y^n)$, by hypothesis, an analytic function which can be expanded in a convergent Taylor series about the origin. Thus,

$$z^i(x, y) = z^i(0, 0) + \sum_{j=1}^{n} \left\{ \frac{\partial z^i(0, 0)}{\partial x^j} x^j + \frac{\partial z^i(0, 0)}{\partial y^j} y^j \right\}$$

$$+ \frac{1}{2} \sum_{j,k=1}^{n} \left\{ \frac{\partial^2 z^i(0, 0)}{\partial x^j \partial x^k} x^j x^k + 2\frac{\partial^2 z^i(0, 0)}{\partial x^j \partial y^k} x^j y^k \right.$$

$$\left. + \frac{\partial^2 z^i(0, 0)}{\partial y^j \partial y^k} y^j y^k \right\} + \cdots.$$

If the coordinate neighborhood is taken sufficiently small, the terms indicated by dots become arbitrarily small with respect to the terms written out. If we set both x and y equal to the identity element, then z will also be the identity element, so that $z^i(0, 0) = 0$. If we set y equal to the identity element, but leave x arbitrary, this must reduce to the equation $z = x$. Hence, we must have

$$\frac{\partial z^i(0, 0)}{\partial x^j} = \delta^i_j,$$

where $\delta^i{}_j$ is the Kronecker delta and

$$\frac{\partial^2 z^i(0,0)}{\partial x^j \partial x^k} = 0.$$

A similar argument can be given by setting x equal to the identity, leaving y arbitrary. We are then left with the series

$$z^i = x^i + y^i + \sum_{j,k=1}^{n} a^i{}_{jk} x^j y^k + \cdots .$$

It seems therefore that the local structure of a Lie group is determined by the tensor $a^i{}_{jk}$. Actually, only the antisymmetric part of this tensor is relevant because its symmetric part can be transformed away simply by introducing a new system of coordinates. Indeed, we need only set

$$(x^i)' = x^i - \frac{1}{2} \sum_{j,k=1}^{n} a^i{}_{jk} x^j x^k .$$

In these coordinates, group multiplication is given locally by

$$(z^i)' = (x^i)' + (y^i)' + \frac{1}{2} \sum_{j,k=1}^{n} (a^i{}_{jk} - a^i{}_{kj})(x^j)'(y^k)' + \cdots .$$

For convenience we may assume that such a coordinate transformation has already been performed beforehand, if necessary, and we henceforth drop the primes. It is not possible by means of further coordinate transformations to eliminate the remaining *structure tensor*

$$c^i{}_{jk} = a^i{}_{jk} - a^i{}_{kj} .$$

It is of interest to study what group operation corresponds to this structure tensor. Our formula shows that in lowest order, group multiplication corresponds simply to addition of the coordinates. Since the coordinates of the identity elements are zero, the coordinates of x^{-1} must in lowest order be $(x^{-1})^i = -x^i$. Thus the operation of taking inverses corresponds to taking negatives of coordinates. To see that this formula also holds in the next order of approximation, we compute the inverse of x as a power series. Since $x \circ x^{-1} = e$, we have

$$0 = (x \circ x^{-1})^i = x^i + (x^{-1})^i + \frac{1}{2} \sum_{j,k=1}^{n} c^i{}_{jk} x^j (x^{-1})^k + \cdots .$$

Solving for $(x^{-1})^i$, we obtain by repeated substitution,

$$(x^{-1})^i = -x^i + \frac{1}{2} \sum_{j,k=1}^{n} c^i{}_{jk} x^j x^k + \cdots .$$

Since $c^i{}_{jk} = -c^i{}_{kj}$, the quadratic term drops out, proving our assertion.

The *commutator* of two group elements x and y is the element $x \circ y \circ x^{-1} \circ y^{-1} = (x \circ y) \circ (y \circ x)^{-1}$; it essentially determines whether x and y commute. Expanding the commutator in a Taylor series, we have

$$(x \circ y \circ x^{-1} \circ y^{-1})^i = (x \circ y)^i + ((y \circ x)^{-1})^i + \frac{1}{2} \sum_{j,k=1}^n c^i{}_{jk} (x \circ y)^j ((y \circ x)^{-1})^k + \cdots$$

$$= \sum_{j,k=1}^n c^i{}_{jk} x^j y^k + \cdots .$$

Thus the tensor $c^i{}_{jk}$ determines the predominant part of the commutator.

The local structure of a Lie group can be summarized conveniently in terms of the tangent space to the Lie group at the identity element. Let $x^1, \cdots, x^n$, as before, be the coordinates of an element x in a neighborhood of the identity in the Lie group. Let $v(x^1, \cdots, x^n)$ be the position vector of this point with respect to the origin of the surrounding Euclidean space. Then the vectors

$$\mathbf{e}_i = (\partial \mathbf{v} / \partial x^i)_0$$

form a basis for the tangent space at the identity element of the Lie group. The coordinates x^i, y^i, z^i of the points of the Lie group close to the origin, used in the previous expressions, can be regarded as components of vectors in the tangent space at the identity. That is, we construct the vectors

$$\mathbf{x} = \sum_{i=1}^n x^i \mathbf{e}_i, \quad \mathbf{y} = \sum_{i=1}^n y^i \mathbf{e}_i \quad \text{and} \quad \mathbf{z} = \sum_{i=1}^n z^i \mathbf{e}_i.$$

The computations given previously can now be interpreted as operations on vectors in this tangent space.

To the lowest order of approximation, the group operation corresponds to vector addition in the tangent space, and taking the inverse of a group element corresponds to taking the negative of the corresponding vector. The operation of taking the commutator of two group elements corresponds in the tangent space to

$$z^i = \sum_{j,k=1}^n c^i{}_{jk} x^j y^k.$$

We can regard this as a form of vector multiplication and introduce the notation

$$\mathbf{z} = [\mathbf{x}, \mathbf{y}].$$

The properties of this vector multiplication follow from the properties of the structure constants $c^i{}_{jk}$. It follows from the definition of the structure constants that they are antisymmetric in their lower indices,

$$c^i{}_{jk} = -c^i{}_{kj}.$$

Therefore, we have

$$[\mathbf{x}, \mathbf{y}] = -[\mathbf{y}, \mathbf{x}].$$

We might ask what further properties c^i_{jk} must have. Substituting the Taylor series for Lie group multiplication into the equation

$$(w \circ x) \circ y = w \circ (x \circ y)$$

and equating the corresponding terms, one obtains expressions relating the c^i_{jk} to coefficients of higher order terms. By permuting the indices cyclically and summing, one can eliminate the coefficients of the higher order terms, obtaining the relation

$$\sum_{k=1}^{n} \{ c^i_{jk} c^k_{lm} + c^i_{lk} c^k_{mj} + c^i_{mk} c^k_{jl} \} = 0.$$

Therefore, our vector multiplication also satisfies the Jacobi identity, and we have a Lie algebra. The tangent vector space at the origin, with this multiplication, is called the *Lie algebra of the Lie group*. In the older literature the Lie algebra was called the *infinitesimal group*. The components of the tensor c^i_{jk} are called the *structure constants* of the Lie algebra with respect to the basis $e_1, \cdots, e_n$.

The local structure of a Lie group, the structure in a sufficiently small neighborhood, is completely determined by the Lie algebra. This is of great importance in applications, for when properties of a local nature are being studied one need only consider the Lie algebra.

1.8 VECTOR FIELDS

We can obtain another picture of the geometrical meaning of the Lie algebra of a Lie group by using the theory of vector fields. We shall sketch this approach here, indicating the main ideas which are involved. The general theory of vector fields applies to any differentiable manifold, not just to Lie groups [126]. To focus on the essential ideas, we consider here just the simplest case of a surface in some Euclidean space which can be specified by a single equation $g(\mathbf{x}) = 0$, where g is a differentiable function. Of course, this discussion could easily be generalized to the case of a surface specified by several such equations.

The gradient ∇g at any point of the surface can be interpreted geometrically as a vector normal to the surface. It is clear that a vector $\mathbf{U}$ is tangent to the surface at the point $\mathbf{x}$ if we have $\mathbf{U} \cdot \nabla g = 0$ at $\mathbf{x}$. The set of all vectors tangent to a differentiable manifold at a point may be regarded as a vector space, which we call the *tangent space* at that point. For a connected differentiable manifold all tangent spaces at all points have the same dimension and this number is called the *dimension* of the manifold.

A *vector field* on a manifold is a differentiable mapping which assigns a tangent vector $\mathbf{U}(\mathbf{x})$ to each point $\mathbf{x}$ on the manifold. If $\mathbf{U}(\mathbf{x})$ and $\mathbf{V}(\mathbf{x})$ are vector fields, then it is clear that any linear combination of them will again be a vector field. Thus the set of all vector fields may be regarded as a vector space. If we set

$$\mathbf{W} = (\mathbf{U} \cdot \nabla)\mathbf{V} - (\mathbf{V} \cdot \nabla)\mathbf{U},$$

then

$$\mathbf{W} \cdot \nabla = (\mathbf{U} \cdot \nabla)(\mathbf{V} \cdot \nabla) - (\mathbf{V} \cdot \nabla)(\mathbf{U} \cdot \nabla).$$

Since $\mathbf{U} \cdot \nabla g = \mathbf{V} \cdot \nabla g = 0$, it follows that $\mathbf{W} \cdot \nabla g = 0$, and hence $\mathbf{W}(\mathbf{x})$ is another vector field. Vector fields form a Lie algebra under this Lie product operation, which we denote by $\mathbf{W} = [\mathbf{U}, \mathbf{V}]$.

For Lie groups we can use the action of the group on itself to associate a certain vector field on the group to each tangent vector at the identity. A path $h(t)$ on a Lie group may be viewed as the trajectory of a particle moving about on the Lie group if we regard t as the time. The velocity of the particle at any point on the path is a tangent vector at that point. If $\mathbf{v}$ is a tangent vector at the identity, we may choose a path $h(t)$ passing through the identity with velocity $\mathbf{v}$ at time $t = 0$. The action of an element g of the group carries this path into a path $g \circ h(t)$ passing through the point g at time $t = 0$ with a certain velocity, which is a tangent vector at g. This tangent vector at g actually depends only on the vector $\mathbf{v}$, and not on the particular choice for the path $h(t)$.

In this way we obtain a vector field on the Lie group, called the *left-invariant vector field* determined by the tangent vector $\mathbf{v}$ at the identity. These left-invariant vector fields form a vector space isomorphic to the tangent space at the identity. Moreover, the Lie product of two left-invariant vector fields is again a left-invariant vector field, so that these vector fields form a subalgebra of the Lie algebra of all vector fields on the Lie group. The Lie algebra of a Lie group may then be defined as this Lie algebra of left-invariant vector fields on the group, this new definition being equivalent to our old one.

1.9 LIE THEORY OF ONE-PARAMETER GROUPS

The abstract definition of a Lie group as a manifold was an outgrowth of the way Lie groups first appeared in the theory of differential equations. Lie groups at first arose as transformation groups and only later were studied as abstract groups. The shift of emphasis from transformation groups to abstract groups in the Lie theory parallels the corresponding development which took place in the theory of finite groups. The theory of Lie groups, originally called the theory of *continuous groups*, was developed by Sophus Lie in connection with the problem of integrating systems of differential equations. Thus, groups with analytic structure arose from the study of the solution of differential equations, just as finite group theory arose in the study of algebraic equations. Since Lie's work is still not widely appreciated, we present a brief indication of his methods [63], [130].

Suppose we are presented with a first order differential equation

$$M(x, y)\, dx + N(x, y)\, dy = 0$$

with analytic coefficients. There exists a one-dimensional Lie group of transformations of the (x, y)-plane which acts analytically and leaves the solutions of the differential equation invariant. If we know beforehand how this group acts on the plane, we can use this knowledge to find the solutions of the differential equation.

An *orbit* is the path of a given point under the action of the group of transformations. We say that a group *acts analytically* if the x and y co-ordinates along any orbit are analytic functions of the local coordinates in the group. We say that the solutions are *invariant* under the action of a group element if it carries any given solution curve into another solution curve. Knowing the orbits, one can introduce canonical coordinates (u, v) in the plane such that the action of the group leaves u invariant, while v is additive in the sense that if g_1 carries (u, v) to $(u, v + \delta_1)$ and g_2 carries (u, v) to $(u, v + \delta_2)$, then $g_1 g_2$ carries (u, v) to $(u, v + \delta_1 + \delta_2)$.

Lie showed that in these coordinates the variables separate, so the differential equation is reduced to quadratures. He also gave an integrating factor for the differential equation in terms of the tangent vectors to the orbits, from which the solution may again be obtained by quadrature. Explicitly, if $P(x, y)$ and $Q(x, y)$ are the components of the tangent vector to the orbit through (x, y), then $(PM + QN)^{-1}$ is an integrating factor. If one knows a two-dimensional transformation group leaving the differential equation invariant, then even the quadrature can be eliminated. In this case, the solutions may be obtained simply by setting the ratio of two independent integrating factors equal to an arbitrary constant.

If we associate the operator

$$U = P\frac{\partial}{\partial x} + Q\frac{\partial}{\partial y}$$

with the group and the operator

$$A = N\frac{\partial}{\partial x} - M\frac{\partial}{\partial y}$$

with the differential equation, then the equation is invariant under the group if and only if

$$UA - AU = \lambda(x, y)A.$$

While every first order differential equation can be shown to be invariant under some one-dimensional Lie group, this is not the case for higher order differential equations. When a higher order differential equation is invariant under a one-dimensional group of transformations, one can reduce the order of the differential equation by one upon introducing new coordinates. One needs to find nontrivial functions $u(x, y)$ and $v(x, y, dy/dx)$ which are invariant under the group. We may mention one example of this general procedure which frequently arises. In many applications one deals with equations which are invariant with respect to changes of the units used for measuring the quantities which appear in them. Then the process of finding u and v can be carried out simply by performing a dimensional analysis of the units for these quantities [34]. When the differential equation is formulated in terms of u and v its order is one less than the order of the original equation. If the dimension of the Lie group under which the differential equation remains invariant is greater than one, the integration procedure can again be simplified by introducing canonical coordinates. These canonical coordinates and the integration procedure depend in general on the structure of the Lie algebra of the group of transformations and on the relative dimensions of the group and the orbits. The dimension of an orbit may well be less than the dimension of the group itself. For instance, the group $SO(3, \mathbb{R})$ is a three-dimensional group of transformations on three-dimensional Euclidean space, while its nontrivial orbits are the spheres which are two-dimensional.

In addition to giving methods of reducing differential equations invariant under a Lie group to quadratures, Lie also showed how to find the differential equations invariant under a given group. The problem of finding invariant differential equations has many applications. For example, in relativistic quantum field theory, a basic problem is that of finding all wave equations invariant under the Lorentz group [66]. The problem simplifies somewhat for the case of zero-mass wave equations because in that case relativistic invariance implies invariance under the bigger group of conformal transformations [95].

The problem of finding differential equations invariant under a given Lie group also comes up in quite different fields. We mention here some work by Hoffman on pattern recognition in visual perception [125]. On the basis of physiological studies of electrical activity in the brain, he postulates that the visual integrative process is based on a first order differential equation, with electrical patterns in the brain embodying information about the isoclines of the differential equation. In order for recognition of a pattern as an entity to occur, as required by the Gestalt theory, this differential equation must be invariant under the group of transformations which leave the pattern recognizable. Hoffman determined the class of differential equations invariant under a Lie group which includes translations, rotations and magnifications. The results of this analysis are used to explain and interpret various visual phenomena, including developmental dyslexia, the whirling spirals evoked under flicker, the alpha rhythm and its desynchronization, and Mackay's complementary after-images.

1.10 MATRIX LIE GROUPS

We have seen that one of the main reasons for introducing the concept of a Lie group is to enable us to treat the classical matrix groups. If we were only interested in these matrix Lie groups, we could even dispense with some of the technicalities of manifold theory [73]. However, this would definitely entail some loss of generality because there do exist Lie groups which are not isomorphic to any matrix group [33].

To prove that the various classical matrix groups are Lie groups, we must show that they are analytic manifolds and that in each case the group operation is analytic. Let us consider first the general linear groups $GL(n, \mathbb{R})$ and $GL(n, \mathbb{C})$. To see that they are manifolds, we embed them in a Euclidean space and simultaneously erect coordinate systems by noting that the n^2 entries of a matrix can be used as the coordinates of a point in a Euclidean space of dimension n^2. For the group $GL(n, \mathbb{C})$, we treat real and imaginary parts of the matrix entries as separate coordinates and so use a real Euclidean space of dimension $2n^2$ rather than a complex space of dimension n^2. Since the determinant is a continuous function in these coordinates, all points sufficiently near a point representing a nonsingular matrix also represent nonsingular matrices. Hence the general linear group is an open subset of Euclidean space, and the Euclidean coordinates may be used as curvilinear coordinates for the general linear group. In the general linear group, with the chosen coordinates, the group operation is ordinary matrix multiplication and the coordinates of the product of two matrices are polynomials in the coordinates of the two factors. The coordinates of the inverse of a matrix are rational functions of the coordinates of the matrix. Since polynomials and rational functions are analytic, we see that the general linear group satisfies the conditions required of a Lie group.

The other classical Lie groups are all subgroups of the general linear group, and can thus also be embedded in a Euclidean space. These groups may be regarded as hypersurfaces or intersections of hypersurfaces in Euclidean space, so that the matrix entries are not all free to vary independently for them. Nevertheless, in each case, appropriate curvilinear coordinates can be found in terms of which matrix multiplication and inversion are analytic, so that these groups are also Lie groups.

Returning to the general linear group of real or complex $n \times n$ matrices, let us compute the structure constants by using the matrix elements as coordinates. To have the coordinates vanish at the identity, we may express the matrix in terms of its difference from the identity, so that for the matrix $[x^{ij}]$ the new coordinates are

$$\bar{x}^{ij} = x^{ij} - \delta^{ij}.$$

The product of two matrices in these coordinates is given by

$$\bar{z}^{ij} = \bar{x}^{ij} + \bar{y}^{ij} + \sum_{k,l,m,p} \delta^i{}_k \delta_{lm} \delta^j{}_p \bar{x}^{kl} \bar{y}^{mp}.$$

Thus we have

$$a^{ij}{}_{kl,mp} = \delta^i{}_k \delta_{lm} \delta^j{}_p.$$

Therefore, the structure constants for the general linear group are given by

$$c^{ij}{}_{kl,mp} = \delta^i{}_k \, \delta_{lm} \, \delta^j{}_p - \delta^i{}_m \, \delta_{pk} \, \delta^j{}_l.$$

The tangent space has for a basis the matrices

$$\partial \bar{x}^{ij} / \partial \bar{x}^{kl} = \delta^i{}_k \, \delta^j{}_l.$$

The tangent space of the general linear group can be identified with the space of all $n \times n$ matrices, including also those which are not invertible. If x and y are tangent vectors (matrices) with components $\bar{x}^{kl}$ and $\bar{y}^{mn}$, then we have $[x, y] = xy - yx$, where the usual matrix multiplication is meant on the right side. We have thus determined the structure of the Lie algebra of the general linear group of any order. The real Lie algebra of $GL(n, \mathbb{R})$ is denoted by $gl(n, \mathbb{R})$, and the real Lie algebra of $GL(n, \mathbb{C})$ is denoted by $gl(n, \mathbb{C})$. In general, the real Lie algebra of a Lie group may be denoted by using the lower case letters corresponding to the letters used to denote the Lie group.

The Lie algebras of many of the classical matrix groups can be determined by means of the exponential mapping. If each matrix in some neighborhood of the identity in a matrix group can be expressed as $\exp(A)$ for A in some linear subspace of the space of square matrices, then this subspace constitutes the tangent space to the group. When endowed with the commutator multiplication, $[A, B] = AB - BA$, this linear subspace of square matrices is the Lie algebra. For example, the real Lie algebra $sl(n, \mathbb{C})$ of the special linear group consists of the matrices with trace zero. The real Lie algebra $o(n, \mathbb{C})$ of the complex orthogonal group consists of all complex antisymmetric matrices of order n, while the Lie algebra $o(n, \mathbb{R})$ consists of the real ones. Similarly, the real Lie algebra $u(n)$ of the unitary group consists of the anti-Hermitian matrices. The tangent space to the intersection of two manifolds at a point is the intersection of their tangent spaces. Hence the Lie algebras of the matrix groups obtained by intersecting $GL(n, \mathbb{C})$, $GL(n, \mathbb{R})$, $SL(n, \mathbb{C})$, $O(n, \mathbb{C})$ and $U(n)$ are simply the intersections of their Lie algebras.

For our final example, let us compute the Lie algebra $so(3, \mathbb{R})$ of the rotation group in ordinary three-dimensional Euclidean space. Our first problem, of course, is to parametrize the matrices of the rotation group. We can give a general formula for the matrix $[a_{ij}]$ corresponding to an arbitrary rotation through an angle

$$\omega = |\boldsymbol{\omega}| = \sqrt{\omega_1^2 + \omega_2^2 + \omega_3^2}$$

about the axis $\boldsymbol{\omega} = (\omega_1, \omega_2, \omega_3)$. For any angle $\omega \neq 0$, we have

$$a_{ij} = \delta_{ij} \cos \omega - \sum_{k=1}^{3} \varepsilon_{ijk} \omega_k \left(\frac{\sin \omega}{\omega} \right) + \omega_i \omega_j \left(\frac{1 - \cos \omega}{\omega^2} \right),$$

where ε_{ijk} is $+1\,(-1)$ if (i, j, k) is an even (odd) permutation of $(1, 2, 3)$ and 0 otherwise. There is actually no singularity at $\omega = 0$, and hence, the parameters $\omega_1, \omega_2, \omega_3$ can be used as local coordinates for a chart at the identity element of the group $SO(3, \mathbb{R})$. The tangent space at the identity has as a basis the three matrices e_k having (ij)-entry

$$(e_k)_{ij} = (\partial a_{ij}/\partial \omega_k)_{\omega=0} = -\varepsilon_{ijk}.$$

Thus,

$$e_1 = \begin{bmatrix} 0 & 0 & 0 \\ 0 & 0 & -1 \\ 0 & 1 & 0 \end{bmatrix}, \qquad e_2 = \begin{bmatrix} 0 & 0 & 1 \\ 0 & 0 & 0 \\ -1 & 0 & 0 \end{bmatrix}$$

and

$$e_3 = \begin{bmatrix} 0 & -1 & 0 \\ 1 & 0 & 0 \\ 0 & 0 & 0 \end{bmatrix}.$$

Then an element of the Lie algebra $so(3, \mathbb{R})$ is an antisymmetric matrix

$$\omega_1 e_1 + \omega_2 e_2 + \omega_3 e_3 = \begin{bmatrix} 0 & -\omega_3 & \omega_2 \\ \omega_3 & 0 & -\omega_1 \\ -\omega_2 & \omega_1 & 0 \end{bmatrix}.$$

The Lie product is given by

$$[e_i, e_j] = e_i e_j - e_j e_i = \sum_{k=1}^{3} \varepsilon_{ijk} e_k.$$

If we identify the vectors e_i with the usual unit vectors of vector analysis, we recognize this to be the ordinary vector cross product. Therefore, the Lie algebra $so(3, \mathbb{R})$ of the rotation group is isomorphic to the three-dimensional real Euclidean space with the vector cross product as the Lie multiplication. Of course, we could equally well have arrived at the cross product algebra in this case by using the exponential mapping.

1.11 POISSON BRACKETS

Lie algebras play a fundamental role in the study of conservation laws in both classical and quantum mechanics. We briefly sketch here the general framework of the classical theory of conservation laws, using Poisson brackets.

Let us recall how Poisson brackets are used in classical mechanics to rewrite Newton's equations of motion in a canonical form. Newton's laws give differential equations for the trajectory of a mass point moving in three-dimensional Euclidean space or along some curve or surface in Euclidean space. We can also deal with a system of N mass points moving in three-dimensional Euclidean space by regarding them as a single point in a

$3N$-dimensional space. Many problems in classical mechanics are best treated in terms of *curvilinear* or *generalized coordinates* $q^1, \cdots, q^n$ instead of in rectangular Cartesian coordinates. In this case, Newton's laws for a system of particles may be considered as equations of motion for a single point in a *configuration space*, which we assume to be a differentiable manifold. As time varies, the point representing the system moves along a path in configuration space called the *trajectory* of the system. Newton's equations involve both velocity and acceleration, and are thus second order differential equations, but they can be replaced by a set of first order differential equations if we introduce the velocities $\dot{q}^i = dq^i/dt$ as additional variables. The position and velocity of the system can then be specified by a set of $2n$ coordinates $(q^1, \cdots, q^n, \dot{q}^1, \cdots, \dot{q}^n)$ for a point on another manifold called the *tangent bundle* of the configuration space [1]. In these coordinates, Newton's equations may be rewritten in a certain canonical fashion by using the Lagrangian formalism.

The *Lagrangian* $L(q^1, \cdots, q^n, \dot{q}^1, \cdots, \dot{q}^n)$ of a system of particles may be regarded as a smooth function defined on the tangent bundle manifold. The trajectories of a mechanical system are paths on this manifold satisfying *Lagrange's equations*,

$$\frac{d}{dt}\left(\frac{\partial L}{\partial \dot{q}^i}\right) - \frac{\partial L}{\partial q^i} = 0.$$

Lagrange's equations have the same form in any coordinate system because they are the equations for the extremal curves which minimize a certain integral.

To obtain an even more symmetric formulation for classical mechanics, we must pass from this Lagrangian description to the Hamiltonian description via the Legendre transformation. We introduce the *generalized momenta* p_j associated with the corresponding coordinates q^j by

$$p_j = \partial L/\partial \dot{q}^j,$$

where $j = 1, \cdots, n$. If such an elimination is not possible, it is said that the system has constraints [77], [78]. The space with coordinates $(q^1, \cdots, q^n, p_1, \cdots, p_n)$ is called the *phase space*. The *Hamiltonian* H is a function defined in phase space by

$$H(q, p) = \sum_{i=1}^{n} \dot{q}^i(q, p)p_i - L(q, \dot{q}(q, p)).$$

A given physical system is described by a trajectory in phase space determined by Hamilton's equations of motion, together with suitable initial conditions. *Hamilton's equations*

$$\frac{dq^j}{dt} = \frac{\partial H}{\partial p_j}, \qquad \frac{dp_j}{dt} = -\frac{\partial H}{\partial q^j}, \qquad\qquad j = 1, \cdots, n,$$

are not valid for an arbitrary system of coordinates in phase space. They hold only for certain sets of *canonical coordinates* which split into two sets, a set of position coordinates and the corresponding momentum coordinates.

By a *dynamical variable*, we mean any infinitely differentiable function of the coordinates, momenta and time. The dynamical variables form an infinite-dimensional real Lie algebra with the vector multiplication

$$[A, B] = \sum_{j=1}^{n} \left\{ \frac{\partial A}{\partial q^j} \frac{\partial B}{\partial p_j} - \frac{\partial B}{\partial q^j} \frac{\partial A}{\partial p_j} \right\}.$$

The Lie product $[A, B]$ of two dynamical variables A and B is a dynamical variable called the *Poisson bracket* of A and B. By direct computation one can show that the Poisson bracket satisfies the three axioms for a Lie product: bilinearity, antisymmetry and the Jacobi identity [138]. The Lie algebra of all dynamical variables contains no physical information about the system beyond the number of degrees of freedom since all systems with the same number of coordinates and momenta have isomorphic Lie algebras.

However, the subalgebra of conserved quantities, describing the physical symmetries of the system, is usually of considerable interest. A dynamical variable A is *conserved* if $dA/dt = 0$ is valid identically along every trajectory. In general, the rate of change of a dynamical variable A while the system moves along its trajectory is given by

$$\frac{dA}{dt} = \frac{\partial A}{\partial t} + [A, H].$$

In particular, if the Hamiltonian is not explicitly a function of time, then it is conserved, and if there are no constraints, this is simply the *law of energy conservation*. For any two dynamical variables A, B the preceding equation can be used together with the Jacobi identity to show that

$$\frac{d[A, B]}{dt} = \left[\frac{dA}{dt}, B \right] + \left[A, \frac{dB}{dt} \right].$$

It follows that if A and B are conserved, then the Poisson bracket of A and B is conserved. Also any real linear combination of conserved quantities is conserved, and hence the set of all conserved dynamical variables forms a subalgebra of the Lie algebra of all dynamical variables.

1.12 QUANTUM SYMMETRIES

The discussion of symmetries and conservation laws in quantum mechanics differs considerably from the classical theory. In quantum mechanics, the states of a system are not described by points in a phase space, but are instead described in terms of Hilbert spaces. A *Hilbert space* is a vector space (usually infinite-dimensional) over the complex number field equipped with an inner product and having the property that every Cauchy sequence of vectors converges. The inner product of two vectors Ψ and Φ is denoted by (Ψ, Φ). By a *linear operator* in a Hilbert space we mean a linear transformation whose domain and range are subspaces of the Hilbert space. If a linear operator A has a dense domain, we can define its *adjoint* $A^\dagger$ as follows [80]: The domain of $A^\dagger$ is the set of all vectors Ψ for which $(\Psi, A\Phi)$ is a continuous linear function of Φ on the domain of A. The linear operator $A^\dagger$ is then defined on this domain by the requirement that

$$(A^\dagger \Psi, \Phi) = (\Psi, A\Phi)$$

for all Φ and Ψ in the domains of A and $A^\dagger$, respectively.

An *extension* of a linear operator is a linear operator defined on an extended domain and agreeing with the original operator on the original domain. A linear operator H is *Hermitian* if $H^\dagger$ is an extension of H, and we say that H is *self-adjoint* if $H = H^\dagger$. A *unitary operator* U in a Hilbert space is a linear operator defined on the whole Hilbert space satisfying

$$U^\dagger U = U U^\dagger = 1.$$

Thus, a unitary operator has the property that

$$(U\Psi, U\Phi) = (\Psi, \Phi)$$

for all vectors Ψ and Φ in the Hilbert space. We also have to deal with anti-unitary operators, which are not linear operators at all, but are instead antilinear. An *antilinear operator* A in Hilbert space is a mapping which preserves vector addition, but satisfies

$$A(c\Psi) = c^*(A\Psi)$$

for all complex numbers c and vectors Ψ. Here c^* denotes the complex conjugate of the number c. An *antiunitary operator* A is an invertible anti-linear operator which satisfies

$$(\Psi, \Phi) = (A\Phi, A\Psi)$$

for all vectors Φ and Ψ in the Hilbert space.

We now recall some of the basic ideas and assumptions of quantum mechanics. A *physical system* may be regarded as a reproducible experimental apparatus, and a *state of a system* is the result of a preparation of the system, that is, the previous history of the system. Systems prepared in identical fashions will typically yield different values for measured quantities, and therefore all measurements on systems are to be understood in a statistical sense only. Two methods of preparing the system are considered to lead to the same state if they lead to identical probability distributions for all possible measurements. Thus the state of a system is not really a specific history, but rather an equivalence class of such histories. In quantum mechanics one usually distinguishes between pure states and mixtures. Since the description of mixtures can be reduced to that of the pure states, it is sufficient to deal with the latter. It is assumed that each pure state of a system corresponds to at least one unit vector in a Hilbert space.

If, conversely, every unit vector also corresponds to some physical state, we say that there are no *superselection rules* [227]. The relation between pure states and unit vectors is not one-to-one since it is assumed that unit vectors differing only by a phase factor will correspond to the same state. In the absence of superselection rules, we can describe the relation between Hilbert space and pure states as a mapping of the unit sphere in Hilbert space onto the set of pure states. If Φ and Ψ are unit vectors, then $|(\Phi, \Psi)|^2$ is interpreted as the probability that a system prepared in the pure state corresponding to Φ will be found upon measurement to be in the pure state corresponding to Ψ. Note that states which are indistinguishable by these transition probabilities are considered to be identical states.

A *physical symmetry* is an onto mapping of pure states to pure states which preserves all transition probabilities. The assumption about indistinguishability implies that physical symmetries must also be one-to-one as mappings and hence have inverses. The products and inverses of physical symmetries are again symmetries, and hence the physical symmetries form a group. Wigner discovered that physical symmetries correspond to unitary or antiunitary operators in Hilbert space [19], [249]. This correspondence is again unique only to within phase factors. The group generated by these unitary and antiunitary operators will therefore in general be an extension of the physical symmetry group. Technically, the physical symmetry group will be isomorphic to the quotient group of this group of operators modulo the group of phase factors [211].

Although the descriptions of classical and quantum symmetries appear to be very different, the classical description must of course be a limiting case of the quantum description. There actually is a close relation between the classical and quantum descriptions of dynamics, which historically played an important role in developing quantum mechanics via the *correspondence principle*. The correspondence principle was used to guess the quantum analogues of classical dynamics in the early days of quantum mechanics. Any such method of assigning quantum analogues to classical dynamical variables may be called a *quantization procedure*. Starting with the methods proposed in 1926–1927 by P. A. M. Dirac, J. von Neumann and H. Weyl, a large variety of quantization procedures have been studied over the years [210]. One of the most useful of these quantization methods, due to Dirac, makes use of Lie algebraic ideas. The *Dirac correspondence principle* relates the Poisson brackets of classical mechanics to quantum mechanical commutators [75], [76], [79]. In this theory the classical Lie algebra of dynamical variables is related to a Lie algebra of operators in Hilbert space in quantum mechanics. By using this correspondence principle, we can often discuss symmetries of analogous systems in a parallel fashion. For example, the Kepler problem of planetary motion and the hydrogen atom are analogous systems and so have the same symmetries (the four-dimensional orthogonal group), which we discuss further later on.

The quantum mechanical analogue of the classical dynamical variables is a set of self-adjoint operators in Hilbert space called the set of *observables*. For the constant dynamical variables the corresponding operators are constant real multiples of the identity operator I in Hilbert space. A measurement of an observable A will yield a definite value, say α, only in states described by eigenvectors of A corresponding to the eigenvalue α. We further assume that the observables form a real Lie algebra if the Lie product of observables A and B is defined as a purely imaginary multiple of the commutator $AB - BA$. The possibility of making such an assumption depends, of course, on the existence of a fixed common dense domain in the Hilbert space for all of the observables [96], [97].

The correspondence principle requires that we define the Lie product of observables A and B to be

$$\frac{1}{i\hbar}(AB - BA),$$

where $\hbar$ is the quantum of action (Planck's constant divided by 2π). The relation between classical and quantum mechanics found by Dirac may be formally described as a homomorphism from part of the classical Lie algebra of dynamical variables to part of the quantum Lie algebra of observables. To illustrate this, let us consider the description of a nonrelativistic point particle. If x_i and p_i are the ordinary Cartesian coordinates and momentum components of the particle, then the classical Poisson brackets are

$$[x_i, x_j] = [p_i, p_j] = 0$$

and

$$[x_i, p_j] = \delta_{ij}.$$

The corresponding operator equations in quantum mechanics must be

$$X_i X_j - X_j X_i = P_i P_j - P_j P_i = 0$$

and

$$X_i P_j - P_j X_i = i\hbar \delta_{ij} I,$$

where X_i is the operator corresponding to x_i, and so forth. If we take X_i to be the linear operator corresponding to multiplication of any function $\psi(\mathbf{x})$ by x_i, and P_i to be the differential operator $-i\hbar \partial/\partial x_i$, then a purely formal computation indicates that these commutation relations are fulfilled. In the Schrödinger formulation of nonrelativistic quantum mechanics, these operators are interpreted as Hermitian operators on an appropriate Hilbert space of equivalence classes of square-integrable functions.

The quantization prescription given above is unfortunately not complete. The requirement that the quantization map be a Lie algebra homomorphism does not define it uniquely on the whole set of dynamical variables. To obtain a complete quantization prescription, the ambiguities which remain have to be removed by additional assumptions [108], [250], [251]. In the last analysis, of course, there is no reason to expect that any quantization procedure will be entirely satisfactory for physics. Strictly speaking, the correspondence principle only requires that the classical limit of quantum mechanics be derivable in some precise way, but not necessarily the other way around. Nevertheless, these quantization procedures may be useful to construct mathematical models by which one can test the consistency of some systems of axioms proposed for quantum mechanics. For example, there has been some interest in using quantization procedures to exhibit a nontrivial example of a relativistic quantum field theory [137], [214], [223].

1.13 HARMONIC OSCILLATORS

Harmonic oscillators are important in both classical and quantum mechanics because conservative stable linear systems have positive definite quadratic Hamiltonians and are therefore formally equivalent to collections of harmonic oscillators. For example, electromagnetic radiation is described by the linear Maxwell equations and may be treated as a collection of harmonic oscillators. Again, a dilute gas consisting of a large number of particles may be treated equivalently as a system of sound waves in a continuous medium. Harmonic oscillators are also the basis for many models in molecular, atomic and nuclear physics. Our interest here lies in the fact that the unitary groups arise naturally in the discussion of systems of identical harmonic oscillators [15], [20], [173]. This symmetry is broken if there is any interaction among the oscillators, but cannot be ignored if we use perturbation theory to describe the interaction.

It is easy to exhibit the unitary symmetry of a system of harmonic oscillators directly. We adopt the quantum mechanical point of view because it is simpler, but the same type of discussion can be given in classical mechanics. The Hamiltonian for a system of n identical noninteracting harmonic oscillators is

$$H = \sum_{\alpha=1}^{n} \left\{ \frac{p_\alpha^2}{2m} + \frac{k}{2} q_\alpha^2 \right\}.$$

In discussing harmonic oscillators, it is natural and convenient to choose units in which $m = k = \hbar = 1$. We define *creation* and *annihilation operators* by

$$a_\alpha = \frac{q_\alpha + ip_\alpha}{\sqrt{2}}, \qquad a_\alpha^+ = \frac{q_\alpha - ip_\alpha}{\sqrt{2}},$$

in terms of which the Hamiltonian may be written as

$$H = \text{const.} + \sum_{\alpha=1}^{n} a_\alpha^+ a_\alpha.$$

The creation and annihilation operators satisfy the commutation relations

$$[a_\alpha, a_\beta] = 0, \quad [a_\alpha, a_\beta^+] = \delta_{\alpha\beta}, \quad [a_\alpha^+, a_\beta^+] = 0$$

with each other, and

$$[H, a_\alpha^+] = a_\alpha^+, \qquad [H, a_\alpha] = -a_\alpha$$

with the Hamiltonian. These latter commutation relations imply that if ψ is an eigenvector of H with eigenvalue E, then $a_\alpha\psi$ is either zero or an eigenvector with eigenvalue $E - 1$, while $a_\alpha^+\psi$ is an eigenvector with eigenvalue $E + 1$. Thus the harmonic oscillator has an infinite series of equally spaced levels.

Both the Hamiltonian and the commutation relations are invariant under a unitary transformation,

$$a_\alpha' = \sum_\beta U_{\alpha\beta} a_\beta,$$

so $U(n)$ is a symmetry group of the n-dimensional harmonic oscillator. The corresponding Lie algebra $u(n)$ is spanned by the elements $a_\alpha^+ a_\beta$, which commute with the Hamiltonian operator H.

In classical mechanics, the Hamiltonian

$$H = \frac{1}{2}\sum_\alpha (p_\alpha^2 + q_\alpha^2)$$

appears at first sight to be symmetric under the orthogonal group $O(2n, \mathbb{R})$. However, one must remember that Hamilton's equations hold only for certain canonical systems of coordinates in phase space. In the case of linear transformations of the coordinates $(q^1, \cdots, q^n, p_1, \cdots, p_n)$ in phase space, this requirement limits us to symplectic linear transformations [65]. In view of the isomorphism between $U(n)$ and $Sp(n, \mathbb{R}) \cap O(2n, \mathbb{R})$, we see that the symmetry group of a system of n identical classical harmonic oscillators is again the unitary group [120].

1.14 LIE SUBGROUPS AND ANALYTIC HOMOMORPHISMS

For many of the problems of mathematics and physics in which Lie groups arise, the most interesting information can be derived by looking at their Lie algebras. Therefore, we now return to the study of the relation between Lie groups and Lie algebras, to prepare for a more extensive study of Lie algebras.

In general, a subgroup of a Lie group need not be a Lie group. In order for a subgroup to be a Lie group, it must possess its own atlas of local coordinate systems, in terms of which the group operations are analytic. A *Lie subgroup* of a Lie group is a subgroup which is itself a Lie group and for which the local coordinates in the subgroup are analytic functions of those in the group. The Lie algebra of a Lie subgroup of a Lie group may be naturally identified with a subalgebra of the Lie algebra of the original group. Conversely, every subalgebra of the Lie algebra of a Lie group may be identified with the Lie algebra of a connected Lie subgroup. Every closed subgroup of a Lie group is a Lie subgroup. However, a Lie subgroup of a Lie group need not be a closed subgroup. From the theory of topological groups it is known that every open subgroup is closed, and hence open subgroups of Lie groups are also Lie subgroups [64].

Similarly, a homomorphism between Lie groups in general need not be an analytic mapping. A homomorphism between Lie groups is called an *analytic homomorphism* if the coordinates of the image of a point are analytic functions of the coordinates of the point. Analytic homomorphisms of Lie groups induce homomorphisms of the corresponding Lie algebras. The homomorphism induced by a composition of analytic homomorphisms is the composition of their induced homomorphisms. This relation between homomorphisms of Lie groups and Lie algebras can be used to translate many results about Lie groups into related results about their corresponding Lie algebras. For example, the inclusion mapping for a Lie subgroup is an analytic homomorphism, and hence induces the corresponding embedding for their Lie algebras noted above. It is a remarkable fact that any continuous homomorphism of Lie groups is also analytic [124].

If H is a closed normal subgroup of a Lie group G, then we may regard the quotient group G/H as a Lie group in a natural way, and the natural projection is analytic since it is known to be continuous. Finally, as one might expect, a form of the fundamental theorem of homomorphisms holds for Lie groups, and it is related to the corresponding theorem for their Lie algebras. The kernel of an analytic homomorphism of a Lie group is a closed normal subgroup. The kernel of the induced Lie algebra homomorphism is the Lie algebra of the kernel of the group homomorphism.

1.15 CONNECTED LIE GROUPS

To a large extent, even the global structure of a Lie group is determined by its local structure, that is, by what happens in an arbitrarily small neighborhood of the identity. This is because by multiplying together many elements very near to the identity element, we can obtain elements further away. Also, any neighborhood of the identity can be transported along any arc in arbitrarily small steps, much as one does analytic continuation. One may therefore ask whether the whole Lie group is determined by its Lie algebra, the answer being yes, provided that the Lie group is simply-connected [54], [192]. (The term simply-connected and several other terms used in the following discussion are defined below.) Each real Lie algebra is isomorphic to the Lie algebra of a simply-connected Lie group, which is uniquely determined to within an isomorphism. Hence, a simply-connected Lie group is completely determined by its Lie algebra to within an isomorphism. The proof of this theorem is based on the existence of solutions to certain systems of partial differential equations. The global structure theory for an arbitrary Lie group almost reduces to the study of two discrete Lie groups and one simply-connected Lie group. This reduction proceeds in two stages, the first stage involving the extraction of the identity component, and the second involving passing to the universal covering group. Many of the ideas here are based on the more general theory of topological groups, but for Lie groups some simplifications occur. Lie groups, being manifolds, are locally homeomorphic to open regions of Euclidean space, and therefore have very nice local properties. In particular, every Lie group is a locally compact normal Hausdorff space.

A topological space is *connected* if it has no proper subsets which are both open and closed. An *arc* γ in a topological space is a continuous mapping from the closed interval $[0, 1]$ into the space, and a *loop* is an arc for which $\gamma(0) = \gamma(1)$. A topological space is *arcwise connected* if any two points of the space can be joined by an arc in the space. A manifold is connected if and only if it is arcwise connected, and hence the same is true for Lie groups. A Lie group is *simply-connected* if it is connected and every loop in the group can be continuously shrunk to a point. The real line, regarded as a group under addition, and the unit circle in the complex plane, regarded as a group under multiplication, are both examples of connected Lie groups.

At the other end of the spectrum of Lie groups are the discrete groups. A topological space is *discrete* if every subset is open. A discrete topological group is *totally disconnected* in the sense that no two distinct points can be joined by an arc. Any discrete topological group may be regarded as a Lie group by taking the charts to consist of single points and assigning zero as the coordinate of any point. The Lie algebra of a discrete Lie group consists only of the zero vector, and conversely, if the Lie algebra of a Lie group is zero, then the group is discrete.

A *component* of a Lie group is a maximal connected subset, that is, a subset consisting of all elements which can be joined by arcs to some given element. The component containing the identity element of a Lie group is a closed normal subgroup, and the components of the Lie group are precisely the cosets of this subgroup. Moreover, the identity component G_0 of a Lie group G is an open subgroup, so that the quotient group G/G_0 is not only totally disconnected, but even discrete.

For example, the real general linear group is not connected since there is a surface separating the elements with positive determinants from those with negative determinants. We may picture the group $GL(n, \mathbb{R})$ as filling a real Cartesian space of dimension n^2, except for the surface consisting of the points corresponding to the singular matrices, which divides the space into two connected components. The identity component consists of the elements with positive determinant, and the discrete quotient group in this case is the cyclic group of order two.

The study of a Lie group G does not quite reduce to studying the connected identity component G_0 and the discrete quotient group G/G_0. One also needs to know the action of certain inner automorphisms restricted to the identity component to obtain the complete structure of a Lie group. Frequently, for Lie groups of practical importance, the structure of the quotient group is extremely simple, and knowledge of it together with knowledge of the structure of the identity component is all that is needed to completely determine the group structure.

For the second stage of the reduction of the global structure of a Lie group, our analysis is directed toward the structure of the identity component G_0, which is a connected Lie group. The Lie algebra of the original Lie group is isomorphic to the Lie algebra of the identity component. This Lie algebra is also isomorphic to the Lie algebra of a simply-connected Lie group, which is called the *universal covering group* of the connected Lie group G_0. The Lie group G_0 is the homomorphic image of the simply-connected universal covering group determined by the Lie algebra. The kernel of this homomorphism is a discrete normal subgroup of the universal covering group called the *fundamental group* or Poincaré group [36], [200], [205]. Each point of this discrete fundamental group corresponds to a set of loops in the connected group G_0. Two such loops correspond to the same point of the kernel if and only if one can be continuously transformed into the other.

1.16 ABELIAN LIE GROUPS

We may illustrate some of the results of the global structure theory for Abelian Lie groups. A Lie group is *Abelian* if

$$ab = ba$$

for all elements a and b of the group. The simplest Abelian Lie groups are the vector groups. A *vector group* is a real vector space $\mathbb{R}^n$, regarded as an Abelian Lie group under the operation of vector addition, using any rectilinear coordinate system to provide a chart. Vector groups are simply-connected, and conversely, every simply-connected Abelian Lie group is isomorphic to a vector group. An *Abelian Lie algebra* is a Lie algebra whose structure constants are all equal to zero, so that

$$[x, y] = 0$$

for all elements x and y of the Lie algebra. Note that any real vector space may be made into an Abelian Lie algebra by introducing this trivial multiplication.

We can now use the theory of the universal covering group to classify all the connected Abelian Lie groups. The Lie algebra of any Abelian Lie group is an Abelian Lie algebra, and we may regard the Lie algebra itself as a vector group. Obviously, a vector group is its own tangent space, and so with the trivial multiplication, is its own Lie algebra. Hence, every connected

Abelian Lie group has a vector group as its universal covering group. Every connected Abelian Lie group is then a homomorphic image of a vector group, the kernel being a discrete subgroup. The discrete subgroups of a vector group are crystallographic lattices of vectors of the form

$$n_1\mathbf{e}_1 + \cdots + n_k\mathbf{e}_k,$$

where the n_i run over all integers and the $\mathbf{e}_i$ are fixed linearly independent vectors.

Thus every connected Abelian Lie group is a direct product of lines and circles. The one-dimensional simply-connected Abelian Lie groups are isomorphic to the additive group of the real line. Any discrete subgroup of the real line consists of equally spaced points, all the integer multiples of a fixed real number. Identifying points of the line modulo this discrete subgroup is equivalent to winding the line about a circle of circumference equal to the spacing between the points of the subgroup. If k is the least positive member of the discrete subgroup, then

$$f(x) = \exp\left(2\pi i x / k\right)$$

maps the real line homomorphically onto the circle group, and has the discrete subgroup as kernel. Thus, the circle group has the real line group as its universal covering group, and the discrete fundamental group of the circle group is isomorphic to the additive group of integers. In short, the line and the circle are the only connected one-dimensional Abelian Lie groups. The only two-dimensional connected Abelian Lie groups are the plane, the cylinder and the torus. Note that the plane group may also be regarded as the additive group of all complex numbers, and the cylinder group as the multiplicative group of the nonzero complex numbers. For higher dimensions, the results are similar, there being exactly $n + 1$ different connected n-dimensional Abelian Lie groups.

1.17 LOW-DIMENSIONAL LIE GROUPS

Many Lie groups may be realized as matrix Lie groups. We recall that analytic subgroups of a Lie group correspond to subalgebras of its Lie algebra, and the Lie algebra may be taken to be the tangent space at the identity. The tangent space of a matrix Lie group is some subspace of the tangent space of the general linear group, the latter being identified with the space of all square matrices of a given order. The Lie product in the tangent space of a matrix Lie group is always the commutator, just as it is for the general linear group.

To illustrate this, let us consider the *real affine group* consisting of all real matrices of the form

$$\begin{bmatrix} e^a & b \\ 0 & 1 \end{bmatrix}.$$

We may think of this real affine group as the identity component of the group of inhomogeneous linear transformations on the real line [11], [12]. Since the underlying manifold of the real affine group is a plane with coordinates (a, b), the group is a simply-connected Lie group. A basis for the tangent space consists of the matrices

$$e_1 = \begin{bmatrix} 1 & 0 \\ 0 & 0 \end{bmatrix} \quad \text{and} \quad e_2 = \begin{bmatrix} 0 & 1 \\ 0 & 0 \end{bmatrix}.$$

The Lie product is simply

$$[e_1, e_2] = e_1 e_2 - e_2 e_1 = e_2.$$

In fact, any non-Abelian two-dimensional real Lie algebra has this structure for an appropriate choice of basis. Since this *affine Lie algebra* is the only non-Abelian two-dimensional one, any connected two-dimensional non-Abelian Lie group is isomorphic to the real affine group modulo a discrete normal subgroup. By writing out the form of a conjugate class, it is easily seen that no proper normal subgroup can be discrete. The real affine group is therefore the only connected non-Abelian two-dimensional Lie group. Thus, the only possible connected two-dimensional Lie groups are the plane, the cylinder and the torus. The real Cartesian plane $\mathbb{R}^2$ admits two group structures making it a Lie group, one Abelian and one non-Abelian. The torus and the cylinder admit only an Abelian Lie group structure.

For higher dimensions, finding all connected Lie groups becomes a much more complicated problem. A part of the solution, finding all the possible real Lie algebras of a given dimension, has been studied [174], [175], [176], [177]. We shall say more about this part of the problem later on.

1.18 THE COVERING GROUP OF THE ROTATION GROUP

Since $SO(3, \mathbb{R})$ is connected but not simply-connected, it is the homomorphic image of a simply-connected Lie group having the same Lie algebra. The simply-connected Lie group associated with the vector cross product Lie algebra is the special unitary group $SU(2)$. The homomorphism of $SU(2)$ onto $SO(3, \mathbb{R})$ is of fundamental importance in the Pauli theory of electron spin. The *Pauli matrices* are a set of 2×2 matrices,

$$\sigma_1 = \begin{bmatrix} 0 & 1 \\ 1 & 0 \end{bmatrix}, \quad \sigma_2 = \begin{bmatrix} 0 & -i \\ i & 0 \end{bmatrix} \quad \text{and} \quad \sigma_3 = \begin{bmatrix} 1 & 0 \\ 0 & -1 \end{bmatrix}.$$

The group $SU(2)$ then consists of all 2×2 matrices of determinant one which can be written in the form

$$a1 + ib\sigma_1 + ic\sigma_2 + id\sigma_3,$$

where a, b, c and d are real numbers, and 1 is the identiy matrix. Since the determinant of such a matrix is $a^2 + b^2 + c^2 + d^2$, we see that the group manifold of $SU(2)$ can be identified with the unit sphere in a real four-dimensional Euclidean space with coordinates (a, b, c, d). Thus the special unitary group $SU(2)$ is a simply-connected three-dimensional Lie group [54]. For any Q in $SU(2)$, we define a 3×3 matrix $[a_{ij}]$ by

$$a_{ij} = \tfrac{1}{2} \operatorname{Tr}(Q\sigma_i Q^\dagger \sigma_j),$$

where $Q^\dagger$ is the Hermitian conjugate of Q. The matrix $[a_{ij}]$ is a rotation matrix, and every rotation matrix can be obtained from a matrix Q in $SU(2)$ using this formula. Moreover, two distinct members Q and Q' of the group $SU(2)$ yield the same rotation matrix if and only if $Q' = -Q$. For any pair of traceless 2×2 matrices X, Y we have the identity

$$\tfrac{1}{2} \operatorname{Tr}(XY) = \sum_{i=1}^{3} \tfrac{1}{2} \operatorname{Tr}(\sigma_i X) \cdot \tfrac{1}{2} \operatorname{Tr}(\sigma_i Y).$$

This identity can be used to verify that the mapping of $SU(2)$ onto $SO(3, \mathbb{R})$ is a group homomorphism. By the fundamental homomorphism theorem, the rotation group $SO(3, \mathbb{R})$ is isomorphic to the quotient group of $SU(2)$ modulo its center, the discrete subgroup consisting of the identity and its negative. Incidentally, since the group $SU(2)$ is homeomorphic with the unit sphere in 4-space, it is clearly compact, and the rotation group $SO(3, \mathbb{R})$, being a continuous image of $SU(2)$, is also compact.

    The relationship between the groups $SO(3, \mathbb{R})$ and $SU(2)$ can also be made explicit in the following alternative manner. The elements of $SO(3, \mathbb{R})$ correspond in a one-to-one fashion with the rotations of a sphere about its center. The points of the sphere other than the "north pole" may be identified with the complex plane by the usual projection from the "north pole" onto a plane tangent to the sphere at the "south pole." Under this projection, each rotation of the sphere induces a corresponding mapping of the complex plane onto itself, a complex function of a complex variable. The complex functions found in this way are certain linear fractional transformations of the form

$$f(z) = \frac{\alpha z + \beta}{\gamma z + \delta},$$

where α, β, γ and δ are complex numbers and $\alpha\delta - \beta\gamma \neq 0$. The composition of two such linear fractional transformations is again a linear fractional transformation. Moreover, the condition $\alpha\delta - \beta\gamma \neq 0$ ensures that the transformation has an inverse, which is again a linear fractional transformation.

    The linear fractional transformations form a group, and the rotation group is isomorphic to a subgroup of this group. Obviously $f(z)$ is unchanged if all the coefficients α, β, γ, δ are multiplied by a common factor, so by introducing an appropriate factor we can always make $\alpha\delta - \gamma\beta = 1$. Since only the square of a common factor enters into the expression $\alpha\delta - \gamma\beta$, its negative will serve equally well to satisfy the condition $\alpha\delta - \gamma\beta = 1$. To each such $f(z)$, therefore, there correspond two matrices of coefficients,

$$\begin{bmatrix} \alpha & \beta \\ -\gamma & \delta \end{bmatrix}$$

and its negative, both with determinant one. The linear fractional transformation corresponding to a product of two such matrices is the composition of the linear fractional transformations corresponding to the matrices being multiplied. Thus we have a homomorphism of the group $SL(2, \mathbb{C})$ onto the group of linear fractional transformations, and the kernel of this homomorphism consists of the identity matrix and its negative. Not every linear fractional transformation, however, corresponds to a rotation of a sphere. In fact, the group of linear fractional transformations is isomorphic to the identity component of the Lorentz group. A linear fractional transformation corresponds to a rotation of the sphere if and only if it corresponds to a unitary matrix. That is, its matrix must have the form

$$\begin{bmatrix} a + id & c + ib \\ -c + ib & a - id \end{bmatrix},$$

where a, b, c and d are real numbers. The condition $\alpha\delta - \beta\gamma = 1$ is precisely the condition that the vector (a, b, c, d) lie on the unit sphere in 4-space. Thus again we obtain the homomorphism of $SU(2)$ onto $SO(3, \mathbb{R})$ as before. Diagram 1 summarizes the interrelations between the various groups discussed here.

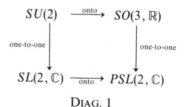

DIAG. 1

Here we have denoted the linear fractional transformation group, or *projective special linear group*, by $PSL(2, \mathbb{C})$.

1.19 TENSOR PRODUCT OF VECTOR SPACES

The study of the local structure of Lie groups, based on the theory of Lie algebras, makes heavy use of linear algebra and vector space concepts. For the complexification process, as well as in connection with the theory of bilinear forms and elsewhere, it is convenient to use a basic concept of vector space theory, the tensor product. We may recall that in the discussion of the geometric concept of orthogonality and in the definition of associative and Lie algebras, we already had to deal several times with bilinear functions.

There are actually several different, but equivalent, ways to define the tensor product of two vector spaces V_1 and V_2. The best way is to give a universal definition, defining the tensor product by means of its properties. Another way, which assures the existence of the object being defined, is to give a completely constructive definition, and this is what we shall do first. We temporarily use the nonstandard but rather suggestive notation $v_1 \times v_2$ for the ordered pair (v_1, v_2) having for its first element a vector v_1 in V_1 and for its second element a vector v_2 in V_2. The set of all such ordered pairs can be regarded as the basis of an infinite-dimensional vector space consisting of all their finite formal linear combinations. A typical vector in this space is a vector

$$\sum_{i=1}^{n} \alpha_i(v_{1i} \times v_{2i}).$$

Consider the set of all vectors in this space of the forms

$$(u_1 + v_1) \times v_2 - u_1 \times v_2 - v_1 \times v_2,$$

$$v_1 \times (u_2 + v_2) - v_1 \times u_2 - v_1 \times v_2,$$

$$\alpha(v_1 \times v_2) - (\alpha v_1) \times v_2$$

and

$$\alpha(v_1 \times v_2) - v_1 \times (\alpha v_2).$$

The quotient space of the whole infinite-dimensional space with respect to the infinite-dimensional subspace spanned by these vectors is called the *tensor product vector space* $V_1 \otimes V_2$. In this construction, the elements of the vector space $V_1 \otimes V_2$, which we may naturally call *tensors*, are of course cosets of vectors in the original space with respect to the subspace. In particular, the coset determined by the ordered pair $v_1 \times v_2$ is a tensor denoted by $v_1 \otimes v_2$ which we call the *tensor product of the vectors* v_1 and v_2.

It follows from the construction that

$$\alpha(v_1 \otimes v_2) = (\alpha v_1) \otimes v_2 = v_1 \otimes (\alpha v_2)$$

for any scalar α, and that

$$(u_1 + v_1) \otimes v_2 = u_1 \otimes v_2 + v_1 \otimes v_2,$$

$$v_1 \otimes (u_2 + v_2) = v_1 \otimes u_2 + v_1 \otimes v_2.$$

If $\{v_{1i}\}$ is a basis for V_1 and $\{v_{2j}\}$ a basis for V_2, then the set of tensors $\{v_{1i} \otimes v_{2j}\}$ is a basis for $V_1 \otimes V_2$. Thus the dimension of the tensor product $V_1 \otimes V_2$ is the product of the dimensions of V_1 and V_2, and any tensor can be written as

$$\sum_{i,j} \alpha_{ij} v_{1i} \otimes v_{2j}.$$

The array of coefficients α_{ij} is uniquely determined by the tensor being represented, and it changes appropriately when the bases in V_1 and V_2 are changed [215].

Finally we may note that the construction given above is not the only one possible. Another way to construct the tensor product $V_1 \otimes V_2$ can be given in terms of the dual space of the vector space of all bilinear forms on the Cartesian product $V_1 \times V_2$. For an ordered pair (v_1, v_2) in $V_1 \times V_2$ we let $v_1 \otimes v_2$ be the element of this dual space for which

$$(v_1 \otimes v_2)(\beta) = \beta(v_1, v_2)$$

for all bilinear forms β on $V_1 \times V_2$. The tensor product $V_1 \otimes V_2$ may then be defined as the subspace spanned by the set of all such elements $v_1 \otimes v_2$. In the case of finite-dimensional vector spaces, the subspace $V_1 \otimes V_2$ is in fact the whole dual space of the space of bilinear forms, while in the infinite-dimensional case it is a proper subspace of this dual space [114], [136].

If V_1 and V_2 are vector spaces, then a function $\beta : V_1 \times V_2 \to W$ mapping $V_1 \times V_2$ into W is called a *bilinear mapping* if it satisfies the following properties for any scalars a and b and any vectors x, y, u in V_1 and v, w, z in V_2:

$$\beta(ax + by, z) = a\beta(x, z) + b\beta(y, z),$$

$$\beta(u, av + bw) = a\beta(u, v) + b\beta(u, w).$$

Bilinear forms are of course obtained as a special case of bilinear mappings if we replace the vector space W by the base field. A useful property of the tensor product is that any bilinear mapping $\beta : V_1 \times V_2 \to W$ determines a unique linear mapping $\alpha : V_1 \otimes V_2 \to W$ such that

$$\alpha(v_1 \otimes v_2) = \beta(v_1, v_2)$$

for all v_1 in V_1 and all v_2 in V_2. The process of replacing the bilinear mapping β by the linear mapping α is called *lifting*, and we say that β is *lifted* to α.

Some special cases of the process of lifting bilinear mappings to linear mappings should be mentioned. Any pair of linear mappings between vector space determines a linear mapping between the corresponding tensor product spaces. If $\alpha_1 : V_1 \to V_1'$ and $\alpha_2 : V_2 \to V_2'$ are linear mappings, then we first obtain a bilinear mapping from $V_1 \times V_2$ to $V_1' \otimes V_2'$ which takes the ordered pair (v_1, v_2) into the tensor $\alpha_1(v_1) \otimes \alpha_2(v_2)$. This bilinear mapping can then be lifted to a linear mapping denoted by $\alpha_1 \otimes \alpha_2$ called the *tensor product of the linear mappings* α_1 and α_2. The linear mapping $\alpha_1 \otimes \alpha_2 : V_1 \otimes V_2 \to V_1' \otimes V_2'$ thus obtained has the fundamental property that

$$(\alpha_1 \otimes \alpha_2)(v_1 \otimes v_2) = \alpha_1(v_1) \otimes \alpha_2(v_2).$$

If V is a vector space over the scalar field $\mathbb{F}$, then the mapping which takes (α, v) into αv is a bilinear mapping $\mathbb{F} \times V \to V$, which can be lifted to a linear mapping $\mathbb{F} \otimes V \to V$. This linear map is an isomorphism which may be used to identify $\mathbb{F} \otimes V$ with V, and similarly we may also identify $V \otimes \mathbb{F}$ with V. A *linear form* ξ on a vector space V over a scalar field $\mathbb{F}$ is a linear mapping from V into $\mathbb{F}$. Every finite-dimensional vector space V determines another vector space of the same dimension, the *dual space* V^* consisting of all linear forms on V. The function which takes (ξ, v) into $\xi(v)$ is a bilinear mapping from $V^* \times V$ into $\mathbb{F}$, and consequently can be lifted to a linear mapping from $V^* \otimes V$ into $\mathbb{F}$. The elements of $V^* \otimes V$ are often called *mixed tensors of rank two*, and this linear mapping from $V^* \otimes V$ into $\mathbb{F}$ is then called a *contraction* of such tensors.

If $e_1, \cdots, e_n$ is a basis for V, then the *dual basis* $e^1, \cdots, e^n$ for V^* consists of the linear forms on V satisfying

$$e^i(e_j) = \delta^i_j.$$

A mixed tensor in $V^* \otimes V$ may then be written as

$$\sum_{i,j} \alpha_i{}^j \, e^i \otimes e_j.$$

The subscript and superscript on $\alpha_i{}^j$ are called *covariant* and *contravariant indices*, respectively. Contraction of this tensor yields the scalar $\sum_i \alpha_i{}^i$. Thus contraction in this notation corresponds to setting the upper index of the coefficient array equal to the lower index and summing on it. It is clear that contraction very much resembles the operation of taking a trace. Indeed, they become the same when the spaces $V^* \otimes V$ and $\lin_{\mathbb{F}}(V)$ are identified in a certain natural way.

The process of complexification for a real Lie algebra can be explained as follows. We may recall that a real or complex vector space with a bilinear vector multiplication satisfying the properties

$$[x, y] = -[y, x]$$

and the Jacobi identity

$$[x, [y, z]] + [y, [z, x]] + [z, [x, y]] = 0$$

is called a Lie algebra. If $e_1, \cdots, e_n$ is a basis for a real Lie algebra L, then the Lie product is determined by the structure constants $c_{ij}{}^k$ defined by

$$[e_i, e_j] = \sum_{k=1}^{n} c_{ij}{}^k e_k.$$

Since the definition of a Lie algebra amounts to imposing restrictions on the structure constants, any real Lie algebra L with structure constants $c_{ij}{}^k$ can be extended to a complex Lie algebra having the same structure constants. More formally, if L is a real Lie algebra, then we can form the tensor product space $\mathbb{C} \otimes L$, where the complex number field $\mathbb{C}$ is here regarded as a two-dimensional real vector space. The vector space $\mathbb{C} \otimes L$ may be regarded as a complex vector space since we can define

$$\lambda(\mu \otimes x) = (\lambda\mu) \otimes x$$

for all $\lambda, \mu \in \mathbb{C}$ and all $x \in L$. Finally, the complex vector space $\mathbb{C} \otimes L$ may be regarded as a complex Lie algebra if we set

$$[\lambda \otimes x, \mu \otimes y] = (\lambda\mu) \otimes [x, y],$$

this complex Lie algebra being called the *complexification* of L. Conversely, a complex Lie algebra L may be regarded as a real Lie algebra L^R, since the multiplication of Lie elements by real numbers may be defined simply as the obvious restriction of the multiplication by complex numbers. This Lie algebra L^R is called the *real restriction* of the complex Lie algebra L. Thus we can pass from real Lie algebras to complex Lie algebras, and back again.

1.20 DIRECT SUMS OF VECTOR SPACES

The direct sum, like the tensor product, is a fundamental vector space operation which finds many applications in the theory of Lie algebras and their representations. The direct sum operation in vector space theory is useful both as an analytical tool and as a constructive procedure. Corresponding to these two modes of usage, there are actually two slightly different definitions of the direct sum, known as the internal and the external direct sum. In practice there is little danger in being a bit careless on this point since these two variants are to a large extent equivalent, and the distinction between them can usually be understood from context. If V_1 and V_2 are vector spaces over a field $\mathbb{F}$, their *external direct sum* consists of all the ordered pairs (v_1, v_2), where v_1 is in V_1 and v_2 is in V_2. The external direct sum, denoted by $V_1 \dotplus V_2$, may be regarded as a vector space if vector addition and multiplication of vectors by scalars are defined componentwise. A familiar example of the use of the external direct sum is in the construction of the n-dimensional vector space

$$\mathbb{F}^n = \mathbb{F} \dotplus \cdots \dotplus \mathbb{F} \quad (n \text{ copies})$$

over a field $\mathbb{F}$. Another example of the use of the external direct sum is in the construction of the tensor algebra, to be discussed later.

The concept of internal direct sum is used when we are talking about the lattice of all subspaces of a given vector space. The set of all subspaces of a vector space is closed under the operation of intersection, but not under the operation of union. The *sum* $S_1 + S_2$ of subspaces S_1 and S_2 of a vector space is the set of all elements of the form $x + y$, where x is in S_1, and y is in S_2. Equivalently, the sum of two subspaces may be described as the subspace spanned by their union. The set of all subspaces of a vector space is said to be a lattice under the two operations $\cap$ and $+$. This means that these operations satisfy certain axioms somewhat reminiscent of Boolean algebra, but not quite as strong [112], [134]. In particular, the distributive laws between $\cap$ and $+$ do not hold, and there is no analogue of the de Morgan laws of complementation. More formally, a *lattice* is a partially ordered set in which every pair of elements has a least upper bound and a greatest lower bound. In the case of the lattice of subspaces of a vector space, the partial ordering is just the inclusion relation, while $S_1 \cap S_2$ is the greatest lower bound of S_1 and S_2 and $S_1 + S_2$ is the least upper bound of S_1 and S_2.

The role of complementation in set theory is replaced in vector space theory by the concept of supplement, which is defined in terms of the internal direct sum as follows. The sum of two subspaces is said to be an *internal direct sum* when the intersection of the two subspaces consists of the zero vector. If V is the internal direct sum of subspaces S and T, written $V = S \oplus T$, then every element in V can be written in a unique fashion as the sum of a vector in S and a vector in T. In this case we say that the subspace T is a *supplement* of the subspace S, and conversely. Given any subspace S of a vector space V, there always exists a subspace T such that $V = S \oplus T$, but T is not unique. Thus every subspace has a supplement, but unlike the situation regarding complementation in set theory, supplements are not uniquely determined.

Since the two definitions of direct sum are different, their properties may also be expected to be slightly different. Note that the internal direct sum is only defined for subspaces of a given vector space having zero intersection. The external direct sum on the other hand is defined for an arbitrary pair of vector spaces. Both $\oplus$ and $\dotplus$ satisfy commutative and associative laws, but they are slightly different in detail. For example, although $S_1 \oplus S_2$ is equal to $S_2 \oplus S_1$, the spaces $V_1 \dotplus V_2$ and $V_2 \dotplus V_1$ are in general not equal, but only isomorphic. For vector spaces, a *homomorphism* is any linear mapping, while an *isomorphism* is a one-to-one onto linear mapping. If V is the internal direct sum of two subspaces S_1 and S_2, then V is isomorphic to the external direct sum of S_1 and S_2. Two vector spaces are isomorphic if and only if their dimensions are equal. Therefore, the isomorphism between internal and external direct sums implies that the dimension of the internal direct sum of two subspaces equals the sum of their dimensions.

1.21 THE LATTICE OF IDEALS OF A LIE ALGEBRA

For the structure and classification of Lie algebras, the concepts of subalgebra and ideal play the same fundamental roles that subgroups and normal subgroups play in Lie group theory. If A and B are subspaces of a Lie algebra, we denote by $[A, B]$ the subspace spanned by all vectors $[a, b]$, where $a \in A$ and $b \in B$. A *subalgebra* S of a Lie algebra L is a subspace which is closed under the Lie multiplication, that is, which satisfies $[S, S] \subset S$. An *ideal* I of a Lie algebra L is a subalgebra such that the Lie product of an element of L with any element of I is in the subalgebra I, that is, for all $x \in L$ and all $y \in I$, we have $[x, y] \in I$. Thus, an ideal I of a Lie algebra L may be defined as a subspace which satisfies $[L, I] \subset I$. As may be expected, subalgebras and ideals figure in the fundamental homomorphism theorems for

Lie algebras. In particular, the kernel of any Lie algebra homomorphism is an ideal, while the image is a subalgebra.

The sum and intersection of ideals of a Lie algebra are again ideals, and the ideals of a Lie algebra form a lattice under these two operations. In addition, it follows from the Jacobi identity that the Lie product $[I_1, I_2]$ of two ideals is again an ideal. The situation regarding subalgebras is a little bit different since the sum of two subalgebras need not be a subalgebra, although the intersection of any set of subalgebras is still a subalgebra. Nevertheless, the subalgebras of a Lie algebra still form a lattice. For both the lattice of ideals and the lattice of subalgebras, the partial ordering is inclusion and the greatest lower bound is intersection. In the lattice of ideals, the least upper bound for a pair of ideals is the sum of those ideals. In the lattice of subalgebras, the least upper bound for two subalgebras is not their sum, but rather the intersection of all subalgebras containing their union. Just as in the case of finite groups, the structure of a Lie algebra can be studied by investigating the properties of its lattice of subalgebras [22], [37], [101], [105], [141], [142].

1.22 THE LEVI DECOMPOSITION OF A LIE ALGEBRA

The study of Lie algebras in general can be reduced to the study of two special classes of Lie algebras: solvable Lie algebras and semisimple Lie algebras. These types of Lie algebras may be defined in terms of ideals as follows: With any Lie algebra L, there is associated a *derived series of ideals* defined recursively by

$$L' = [L, L]$$

and

$$L^{(k+1)} = [L^{(k)}, L^{(k)}]$$

for any positive integer k. It is readily proved by induction on k that $L^{(k)}$ is an ideal of L and that the inclusion $L^{(k+1)} \subset L^{(k)}$ holds. We say that L is a *solvable Lie algebra* if the derived series of ideals

$$L \supset L' \supset L'' \supset \cdots$$

is eventually zero. Since a Lie algebra L is Abelian if and only if $[L, L] = 0$, it follows that every Abelian Lie algebra is solvable. The simplest solvable Lie algebra which is not Abelian is the two-dimensional affine Lie algebra. If we choose a basis e_1, e_2 for this Lie algebra such that

$$[e_1, e_2] = e_1,$$

then L' consists of the multiples of e_1, and $L'' = 0$, proving that L is solvable.

In any Lie algebra, the solvable ideals form a sublattice of the lattice of all its ideals, because the sum and intersection of solvable ideals are again solvable ideals. In particular, the sum of all the solvable ideals in a Lie algebra is its unique maximal solvable ideal, called the *radical* of the Lie algebra. We may define a *semisimple Lie algebra* as a Lie algebra which has no Abelian ideals, other than 0. It is easy to see that a semisimple Lie algebra cannot have any solvable ideals either, and hence a Lie algebra is semisimple if and only if its radical is zero.

According to the *Levi theorem* [151], [245], any Lie algebra can be decomposed as the direct sum, in the sense of vector spaces, of its radical R and a semisimple subalgebra S:

$$L = R \oplus S.$$

That is, each element of the Lie algebra can be written uniquely as the sum of an element in the radical and an element of this semisimple subalgebra. Although the radical is uniquely determined, the Levi decomposition is not unique because there may be several suitable semisimple subalgebras. In fact, the Levi decomposition $L = R \oplus S$ is unique only in the trivial case when S is an ideal in L. Malcev, Gotô and Harish-Chandra showed that if there are two Levi decompositions, then there is an automorphism of the whole Lie algebra which carries the one semisimple subalgebra onto the other [104], [117], [160]. The problem of studying the structure of a Lie algebra is thus almost reduced to studying semisimple and solvable Lie algebras.

The only question of structure remaining is to characterize the action of the semisimple subalgebra S on the radical R. To investigate this point, we need to use the methods of representation theory which we are about to discuss. Anticipating a little, we can say that this question boils down to knowing all the modules over a semisimple Lie algebra. Indeed, the condition $[S, R] \subset R$ is equivalent to the statement that we may regard the radical R as a module over the semisimple Lie algebra S.

1.23 SEMISIMPLE LIE ALGEBRAS

To study the structure of semisimple Lie algebras, one uses the fact that they can be decomposed in terms of simple Lie algebras. A *simple Lie algebra* is a non-Abelian Lie algebra which has no proper ideals at all. Every simple Lie algebra is, as one would expect, semisimple, for the only nonzero ideal is the whole algebra; if $L' = L$, this is not solvable, while if $L' = 0$, then L is Abelian and consequently not simple. An example of a simple Lie algebra is the real Lie algebra $so(3, \mathbb{R})$, the familiar three-dimensional vector space $\mathbb{R}^3$ equipped with the usual vector cross product. To see this, we must argue that there are no proper ideals in the Lie algebra $so(3, \mathbb{R})$. Such an ideal would be a proper subspace S of $\mathbb{R}^3$, a line or a plane passing through the origin such that the vector cross product $\mathbf{x} \times \mathbf{y}$ of any vector $\mathbf{x}$ in S by a vector $\mathbf{y}$ in $\mathbb{R}^3$ must lie in S. Since the cross product of two vectors is perpendicular to both and is nonzero unless the two vectors are collinear or at least one is zero, no line or plane can have this property.

The fact that the rotation group $SO(3, \mathbb{R})$ is simple (has no proper normal subgroups) almost follows from the simplicity of its Lie algebra. Since the closure of a normal subgroup is again normal and since the Lie algebra of a closed normal subgroup of $SO(3, \mathbb{R})$ is an ideal of its Lie algebra, we only have to rule out discrete and dense normal subgroups. A normal subgroup of $SO(3, \mathbb{R})$ is *dense* if its closure is all of $SO(3, \mathbb{R})$. If g is an element of any normal subgroup S of $SO(3, \mathbb{R})$, then all elements hgh^{-1} which are conjugate to g must also be in S. But this is equivalent to saying that every rotation about any axis by an angle equal to that of the rotation g about its axis must be in S. If g is not the identity, multiplying it by the inverse of a rotation hgh^{-1} about an axis which has been shifted a small amount, we obtain an element $ghg^{-1}h^{-1}$ in S which is not the identity, but as close to it as we wish. In this way one can further argue that any proper normal subgroup contains a whole neighborhood of the identity element. Since any neighborhood of the identity generates the whole rotation group, it follows that $SO(3, \mathbb{R})$ cannot have any proper normal subgroups at all.

Any semisimple Lie algebra S can be written as a direct sum of simple ideals,

$$S = S_1 \oplus \cdots \oplus S_k.$$

The elements of distinct S_i must commute since a Lie product of elements from distinct S_i must be in their intersection which is zero. Hence, the structure of a semisimple Lie algebra is completely determined by the structure of its simple ideals. Combining these results with Levi's theorem allows us to reduce any Lie algebra to simple and solvable Lie algebras. Thus any Lie algebra L may be written as

$$L = R \oplus (S_1 \oplus \cdots \oplus S_k),$$

where R is a solvable ideal and $S_1, \cdots, S_k$ are simple. However, it should be noted that the S_i are ideals of S, but not necessarily ideals of L.

The above theory can be best illustrated by an elementary example. Perhaps the most familiar example of a Levi decomposition is that of the Lie algebra of the group of all Euclidean motions. In this case the radical is not only solvable, but even Abelian, and the semisimple subalgebra in the Levi decomposition is simple. The radical consists of the subalgebra corresponding to translations or parallel displacements of $\mathbb{R}^3$. The simple subalgebra is isomorphic to $so(3, \mathbb{R})$ and corresponds geometrically to rotations about some fixed point of $\mathbb{R}^3$. The nonuniqueness of the Levi decomposition in this example comes from the arbitrariness of the choice of the fixed point for these rotations.

1.24 THE BAKER–CAMPBELL–HAUSDORFF FORMULA

As an application of the Levi structure theorem, we shall discuss some applications to the theory of differential equations. We have of course already discussed the original work of Lie on differential equations. Recent work on the application of Lie groups and Lie algebras to differential equations has dealt with problems somewhat different from those studied by Sophus Lie. One example is the study of equations of the type

$$dU(t)/dt = A(t)U(t),$$

where U and A are operators and $U(0) = 1$ is the identity. This equation comes up in quantum mechanics as the Schrödinger equation for the evolution operator $U(t)$ of a system whose Hamiltonian operator is $A(t)$, except for a constant factor. Magnus gave a formal solution

$$U(t) = \exp \Omega(t)$$

for this problem, which converges in some interval about $t = 0$ if the operators are finite matrices and A is a continuous function of t (see [159]).

Wichmann and Norman and Wei treated the case

$$A(t) = \sum_{i=1}^{n} a_i(t)X_i,$$

where the constant operators $X_1, \cdots, X_n$ span a finite-dimensional Lie algebra [184], [185], [236], [246]. This situation arises in certain problems of control theory [150]. Here the functions $a_i(t)$, known as *scalar controls*, are piecewise constant functions of time rather than continuous functions. In control theory, the operators $U(t)$ act on the states of the control system, and describe how the states are transformed as a function of time. In this case, the solution can be given locally in the form treated by Magnus as

$$U(t) = \exp \left(\sum_{i=1}^{n} f_i(t)X_i \right).$$

Norman and Wei show that a solution can also be written as a product

$$U(t) = \exp (g_1(t)X_1) \cdots \exp (g_n(t)X_n).$$

These authors also studied the conditions under which the solutions converge globally, that is, for all t.

In control theory, one frequently wants to know whether a system can be adequately steered by a given set of controls [139]. In general, the states that can be reached after a finite length of time from a given initial state under a suitable class of controls form a certain submanifold of the state space. A system is *completely controllable* if for any pair of states, there is a time interval and a control on that interval such that the system trajectory, starting in the one state, and steered by the control, ends at the other. The *isotropy subgroup* of a given state consists of those control processes which, when applied to the system initially in the given state, at the end return the system to that same state. If a system is completely controllable, the state space itself can be identified with the coset space of the group of all control processes modulo the isotropy subgroup of any fixed state [40]. Kucera and Elliott have shown that a system is completely controllable if it is controllable locally in a certain sense [85], [86], [149], [150].

The point of departure for much of this work is a pair of formulas of Baker and Hausdorff which give $\log(e^x e^y)$ and $e^{-x} y e^x$ in terms of commutators of x and y. The first few terms of the expansions are

$$e^{-x} y e^x = y + [x, y] + \frac{1}{2!}[x, [x, y]] + \cdots$$

and

$$\log(e^x e^y) = x + y + \tfrac{1}{2}[x, y] + \tfrac{1}{12}\{[[x, y], y] + [[y, x], x]\} + \cdots.$$

The omitted terms in both of these expansions involve successively higher and higher order commutators of x and y. A computer program to develop the coefficients of the Baker–Hausdorff formula has been written recently [107]. The formula for $\log(e^x e^y)$ in general may fail to converge even in the simplest case when x and y are finite matrices [16], [44], [118]. Magnus gives a formula for $\Omega(t)$ by developing a continuous analogue of the Baker–Hausdorff formula for $\log(e^x e^y)$, while Norman and Wei use the formula for $e^{-x} y e^x$ to obtain differential equations for the functions $g_i(t)$. Conditions for the solutions to be global can sometimes be stated in terms of the structure of the Lie algebra generated by $A(t)$.

Wichmann has utilized the Levi decomposition of finite-dimensional Lie algebras to show that the problem of solving the differential equation can actually be reduced to the case where the Lie algebra generated by $A(t)$ is simple. The Lie algebra generated by $A(t)$ can be decomposed as the direct sum of its radical and a semisimple subalgebra. Wichmann decomposes $A(t)$ as

$$A(t) = A_1(t) + A_2(t),$$

where A_1 is in the radical and A_2 is in the semisimple subalgebra. The original problem may then be reduced to solving two simpler problems. The first of these problems is that of solving

$$dU_2(t)/dt = A_2(t)U_2(t), \qquad U_2(0) = 1,$$

where $A_2(t)$ generates a semisimple Lie algebra. The second problem is that of solving

$$dU_1(t)/dt = (U_2^{-1}(t)A_1(t)U_2(t))U_1(t),$$

also subject to the initial condition $U_1(0) = 1$. If one can find a solution of the first problem, then it is shown that the second problem can be reduced to quadratures. The net effect is thus to reduce the case of a general Lie algebra to the case of a semisimple Lie algebra. The semisimple subalgebra can be further decomposed as the direct sum of its simple ideals. Thus we may decompose A_2 as

$$A_2(t) = A_{21}(t) + \cdots + A_{2k}(t),$$

where the A_{2i} belong to those simple ideals, and hence mutually commute. The first problem may then be shown to reduce to solving the problems

$$dU_{2i}(t)/dt = A_{2i}(t)U_{2i}(t), \qquad U_{2i}(0) = 1.$$

Chen has considered another problem,

$$dx/dt = U(t, x),$$

which can be regarded as the problem of studying a flow with a variable velocity field [52], [53], [122]. An infinitely differentiable vector field can be regarded as an operator on the infinitely differentiable scalar functions by identifying its direction with the directional derivative. Thus we identify the vector field U with its dot product $U \cdot V$ with the gradient operator. The set of such operators forms a Lie algebra under commutation, and therefore by this identification we can also regard the vector fields themselves as forming a Lie algebra. That is, the Lie bracket of two vector fields is the vector field

$$[U_1, U_2] = (U_1 \cdot V)U_2 - (U_2 \cdot V)U_1.$$

We consider here $U(t, x)$ not as a single vector field, but as a one-parameter family of vector fields, indexed by the time t. This family of vector fields generates a certain Lie algebra of vector fields under the Lie bracket composition. Chen shows that if the Lie algebra generated in this manner is finite-dimensional, then the Levi structure theorem can again be used to obtain an analogue of Wichmann's decomposition for the flow problem. This depends basically on developing a more general transformation playing the role of the similarity transformation appearing in Wichmann's differential equation for A_1.

CHAPTER 2

REPRESENTATION THEORY

2.1 LIE GROUP REPRESENTATIONS

One of the main tools in applications of the Lie theory is the concept of a representation. A *representation* of a group is a homomorphism of the group into a group of linear operators on a vector space. In many applications it is sufficient to treat representations in a fairly loose manner. For example, one speaks of vectors, tensors, pseudoscalars, spinors and the like as being various types of geometrical objects, such as directed arrows, ellipsoids, and so on [39], [208]. Representations of the rotation group crop up throughout mathematical physics in the form of spherical harmonics and Legendre functions, multipole expansions and so forth. The actual representation concept is often held in the background. We must of course make this intuitive conception more precise, and moreover we want to make our discussion apply to any Lie group, not just to the rotation group. However, we shall restrict our attention to analytic homomorphisms, and we assume that all vector spaces have finite dimension.

We define a *finite-dimensional representation* of a Lie group to be an analytic homomorphism of the Lie group into the general linear group of invertible linear operators on a finite-dimensional vector space. By fixing a basis in the vector space, we obtain a corresponding homomorphism onto a matrix group. Since analytic homomorphisms of Lie groups induce homomorphisms of the corresponding Lie algebras, every finite-dimensional representation of a Lie group induces a representation of its Lie algebra.

A *representation* of a Lie algebra L consists of a vector space V and a homomorphism f from L into the Lie algebra of all linear operators on V. The term "representation" strictly refers to the pair (V, f), but colloquially it is often used to refer just to the homomorphism f alone. The requirement that f be a homomorphism means that if x is in L, then $f(x)$ is a linear operator on V, and $f(x)$ depends on x linearly:

$$f(c_1 x_1 + c_2 x_2) = c_1 f(x_1) + c_2 f(x_2)$$

for all x_1, x_2 in L and all scalars c_1 and c_2. Also we must have

$$f([x_1, x_2]) = f(x_1)f(x_2) - f(x_2)f(x_1).$$

51

The correspondence between representations of Lie groups and those of Lie algebras is not one-to-one, however, because a given representation of the Lie algebra of a Lie group need not in general correspond to any representation of the Lie group. Nevertheless, the major portion of work involved in studying the group representations is frequently done when one has found those of the Lie algebra.

A simple example of a Lie algebra representation which arises naturally is the adjoint representation of any Lie algebra L. Each element x in the Lie algebra L gives rise to a linear operator ad x acting in L, defined for all y in L by

$$(\text{ad } x)y = [x, y].$$

The operator ad x behaves just like a first order differential operator in that it obeys the Leibniz rule for operating on a product,

$$(\text{ad } x)[y, z] = [(\text{ad } x)y, z] + [y, (\text{ad } x)z].$$

Although this Leibniz rule is merely another way of writing the Jacobi identity, this analogy with differential operators is frequently useful in Lie algebraic computations. We note parenthetically that we may use the operator ad x to rewrite one of the symbolic Baker–Hausdorff formulas as

$$e^x y\, e^{-x} = e^{\text{ad } x} y.$$

The other Baker–Hausdorff formula may likewise be written as

$$\log(e^x e^y) = x + \int_0^1 d\lambda\, \psi(e^{\text{ad } x}\, e^{\lambda \text{ad } y})y,$$

where

$$\psi(t) = \frac{t \log t}{t - 1}.$$

The mapping ad which takes x into ad x is a linear mapping from the Lie algebra L into the space of linear operators on L. To show that it is a representation we need only verify that it preserves Lie products,

$$[\text{ad } x, \text{ad } y] = \text{ad } [x, y].$$

But for any element z in the Lie algebra,

$$[\text{ad } x, \text{ad } y]z = (\text{ad } x)(\text{ad } y)z - (\text{ad } y)(\text{ad } x)z$$

$$= [x, [y, z]] - [y, [x, z]].$$

Using the Jacobi identity and antisymmetry, we have

$$[\text{ad } x, \text{ad } y]z = [[x, y], z] = (\text{ad } [x, y])z,$$

so that ad is indeed a Lie algebra homomorphism. The pair (L, ad) is then a representation of the Lie algebra L, called the *adjoint representation* of the Lie algebra L.

The adjoint representation can be used to define a certain bilinear form, due to Killing, which is of great importance for the structure theory of Lie algebras. The *Killing form* is a symmetric bilinear form defined for any finite-dimensional Lie algebra L by

$$(x, y) = \text{Tr}_L (\text{ad } x)(\text{ad } y).$$

The Killing form permits geometrical ideas such as orthogonality to be used in the study of a Lie algebra. The Killing form is invariant under every automorphism α of the Lie algebra:

$$(\alpha x, \alpha y) = (x, y).$$

The importance of the Killing form derives in part from the fact that a Lie algebra is semisimple if and only if its Killing form is nonsingular. Solvability can also be characterized in a simple way in terms of the Killing form. A Lie algebra L is solvable if and only if the Killing form is zero on the derived algebra $L' = [L, L]$, that is, if $(x, y) = 0$ for all x and y in L'.

A *linear Lie algebra* is a Lie algebra whose elements are linear operators in some vector space, and whose Lie product is the commutator. A representation is *faithful* if it is a one-to-one mapping. If a Lie algebra has a faithful representation, then the Lie algebra is isomorphic to the image of the representation, which is a linear Lie algebra. For a semisimple Lie algebra, the adjoint representation is faithful. For if x belongs to the kernel of ad, then for any y in L we have

$$[x, y] = (\text{ad } x)y = 0,$$

and hence this kernel is an Abelian ideal of L. Consequently if L is semisimple, then this Abelian ideal in L must be zero, and hence, the adjoint representation is faithful. But the adjoint representation need not be faithful for Lie algebras in general. Ado proved that every finite-dimensional Lie algebra has a faithful finite-dimensional representation [2]. Therefore, every finite-dimensional Lie algebra is isomorphic to a Lie algebra of linear operators, and hence, choosing a basis, to a Lie algebra of matrices. One of the ideas involved in the proof of the Ado theorem is the use of the Levi decomposition to reduce the theorem to the case of a solvable Lie algebra. For a solvable Lie algebra one can prove the Ado theorem by induction on the dimension.

2.2 MODULES OVER LIE ALGEBRAS

In some respects the concept of a representation is unnecessarily complicated. The object being represented, Lie group or Lie algebra, is first mapped by a homomorphism into a similar object composed of linear operators which in turn act on a vector space. There is no loss of generality, of course, if we regard the elements of the original object as affecting the linear transformations on the vector space directly, disregarding the intermediate homomorphism. When we take this viewpoint and the object being represented is a group, we speak of the vector space as a module over the group. When we are dealing with an algebra, we refer to the vector space as a module over the algebra.

A *module over a Lie algebra* L consists of a vector space M and a bilinear mapping $L \times M \to M$, called the *module product rule*, such that if the element in M assigned to x in L and v in M is denoted by xv, then

$$[x_1, x_2]v = x_1(x_2 v) - x_2(x_1 v)$$

for all x_1 and x_2 in L and all v in M. As usual, we can feel free to replace the bilinear mapping $L \times M \to M$ by an equivalent linear mapping $L \otimes M \to M$, if we prefer to do so.

The study of modules over an algebra is really the same as the study of the representations, the only difference being a point of emphasis. If M is a module over a Lie algebra L, then for any x in L, let $f(x)$ be the linear operator on M which maps v in M into the vector xv in M. Then (M, f) is a representation of the Lie algebra L. Conversely, given a representation (M, f) we can make the vector space M into a module by defining the product xv of x in L and v in M to be $f(x)v$. Thus the concepts of module and representation are equivalent. In talking about modules we emphasize the vector spaces involved, whereas in talking about representations, we emphasize the homomorphisms. Generally speaking, the module formulation is the easier to work with.

Representations and modules can be defined for Lie groups as well as for Lie algebras. An *analytic representation* of a Lie group G is a pair consisting of a vector space M and an analytic homomorphism f of G into the Lie group $GL(M)$ of invertible linear operators on M. If n is the dimension of M, then $GL(M)$ is isomorphic to the Lie group $GL(n, \mathbb{C})$ of nonsingular $n \times n$ matrices over $\mathbb{C}$. Hence, a representation of a Lie group corresponds to a matrix representation, that is, a homomorphism of the Lie group into the matrix group $GL(n, \mathbb{C})$.

We may also define a *module M over an associative algebra A* in much the same way that we defined a module over a Lie algebra. The main difference is that the requirement

$$[x, y]v = x(yv) - y(xv)$$

for Lie modules is replaced by the requirement

$$(xy)v = x(yv)$$

for all x and y in A and for all v in M. If the associative algebra A has a unity element e, then we may also want to demand that

$$ev = v$$

hold for all v in the module M.

Lie modules have many applications within Lie algebra theory. For example, the adjoint representation is equivalent to regarding any Lie algebra as a module over itself, the module product being taken to be the Lie product itself. By a slight generalization of this idea, we may also regard any ideal of a Lie algebra L as a module over L. Again, any extension of a Lie algebra L, that is, any Lie algebra containing L as a subalgebra, may be regarded as a module over L. We have already seen that modules enter into the structure of Lie algebras via the Levi decomposition. In this case the radical is a module over the semisimple subalgebra, and the module product is again the Lie product itself. Lie modules also are useful in the further study of the structure of semisimple Lie algebras via the theory of roots. In this case the whole Lie algebra is regarded as a module over a certain Abelian subalgebra, the Cartan subalgebra. We shall come back to this in § 2.7.

Any representation (M, f) of a Lie algebra L can be replaced by a matrix representation. If a basis $e_1, \cdots, e_n$ is selected in the vector space M, then the linear operators $f(x)$ correspond to matrices $[f^i{}_j(x)]$ defined by

$$f(x)e_j = \sum_{i=1}^{n} f^i{}_j(x)\, e_i.$$

The mapping which assigns the matrix $[f^i{}_j(x)]$ to x is called a *matrix representation* of the Lie algebra L. If a different basis is selected for M, of course, the matrices of the matrix representation will all be subjected to a common similarity transformation. Matrix representations related by a common similarity transformation are considered to be *equivalent* or *isomorphic*. Equivalence of Lie group representations is defined just as for Lie algebras. Two matrix representations of a Lie group are *equivalent* or *isomorphic* if they are related by a common similarity transformation.

A *homomorphism* h of one module M over a Lie algebra L into another module N over L is a linear transformation $h: M \to N$ which preserves the multiplication by elements of L, that is,

$$h(xv) = xh(v)$$

for x in L and v in M. If the homomorphism h is one-to-one and onto, and hence invertible, then we call it an *isomorphism*, and we say that the modules M and N are isomorphic to each other. If f is the representation of L associated with the module M and if f' is the representation of L associated with the isomorphic module N, then we have $hf(x) = f'(x)h$, and if h is invertible, we may write this as

$$f'(x) = hf(x)h^{-1}.$$

Such representations, corresponding to isomorphic modules, are called *equivalent* representations. If M and N are isomorphic modules, then there exists a choice of bases for both modules such that the representation matrices thus obtained will be the same for the two modules.

If a module M over a Lie algebra L has a subspace S which remains invariant under the action of L, symbolically $LS \subset S$, then S itself can be regarded as a module over L, and we call it a *submodule* of the module M. That is, a subspace S of a module M is a submodule if xv is in S for all x in L and all v in S. In the physics literature modules are also called *representation spaces*, while submodules are called *invariant subspaces*. The submodules of a Lie module form a lattice under intersection and sum. A module which has no submodules other than zero and itself is called an *irreducible module*, or a *simple module*, and the corresponding representation is then also called *irreducible*. In other words, a representation is irreducible when the representation space has no nontrivial invariant subspace.

Since a module M is a fortiori an Abelian group, and a submodule N is a normal subgroup, we can form the quotient group M/N whose elements are the cosets $v + N$, with v in M. Since N is a vector space, multiplication by complex numbers is well-defined on M/N, and hence M/N is a vector space. Similarly, since N is a module over L, multiplication by elements of L is well-defined on M/N, and hence M/N may be considered as a module over the Lie algebra L, called the *quotient module of M with respect to N*. It is easily shown that if h is a homomorphism of a module M into a module N, then the kernel K of h is a submodule of M, and the quotient module M/K is isomorphic with the image of the homomorphism, which is a submodule of N.

2.3 DIRECT SUM DECOMPOSITIONS OF LIE MODULES

There are several useful ways of combining modules to obtain new ones, the most immediate of these being the direct sum. Since modules over Lie algebras are vector spaces, it is meaningful to talk about their internal and external direct sums as vector spaces. If M_1 and M_2 are modules over a Lie algebra L, their vector space external direct sum $M_1 \dot{+} M_2$ can also be regarded as a module over L by defining the action of L componentwise. Explicitly, the action of any element x of the Lie algebra L on any vector (v_1, v_2) in the external direct sum module $M_1 \dot{+} M_2$ is given by

$$x(v_1, v_2) = (xv_1, xv_2).$$

If a module $M = M_1 \oplus M_2$ is the internal direct sum as a vector space of these submodules M_1 and M_2, then M is isomorphic as a module to the external direct sum module $M_1 \dot{+} M_2$.

If a module M is the direct sum of two nonzero submodules, we say that M is *decomposable*, and the corresponding representation is also said to be decomposable. Otherwise, M is called *indecomposable*. Every finite-dimensional module which is decomposable is a direct sum of indecomposable modules. For the study of finite-dimensional modules over Lie algebras, it suffices to consider the indecomposable modules. Obviously an irreducible module must be indecomposable, but in general an indecomposable module need not be irreducible.

A module which is either irreducible or is the direct sum of irreducible submodules is called a *completely reducible module* or a *semisimple module*. A necessary and sufficient condition for a finite-dimensional module to be completely reducible is that every submodule be a direct summand, that is, for every submodule N there is another submodule N' such that

$$M = N \oplus N'.$$

Every finite-dimensional module over a semisimple Lie algebra is completely reducible. Our attention can thus be directed to a study of the irreducible modules of a semisimple Lie algebra since these form the building blocks from which any other module can be constructed. However, this statement does not hold for Lie algebras in general.

Complete reducibility also holds for modules over compact Lie groups, which simplifies their representation theory substantially [124], [192]. For any representation of a compact group by linear operators on a Hilbert space, the inner product on the Hilbert space can be replaced by another inner product with respect to which the operators are unitary [80], [181]. Thus, only unitary representations, i.e., representations by unitary linear transformations, need be considered when one is dealing with compact groups. We recall that unitary representations are also of interest in quantum mechanics in view of Wigner's unitary–antiunitary theorem. For this application we must of course also treat ray representations, but these can be replaced by ordinary unitary representations of the universal covering group [18]. Every unitary representation of a compact group is a direct sum of irreducible unitary representations acting on mutually orthogonal subspaces. Moreover, the irreducible unitary representations of a compact group are all finite-dimensional [144], [180]. Thus the representation theory of a compact group on a Hilbert space reduces to the study of irreducible unitary representations on finite-dimensional vector spaces. In particular, the rotation group $SO(3, \mathbb{R})$ and its universal covering group $SU(2)$, being compact, can only have finite-dimensional irreducible representations. For a noncompact group there may not exist any nontrivial finite-dimensional unitary representations, so we must also study the infinite-dimensional ones [156].

2.4 LIE MODULE TENSOR PRODUCT

A second useful way of combining Lie modules which arises frequently in applications is by means of the tensor product. Since Lie modules are vector spaces, their tensor products are again vector spaces. The tensor product vector space $M_1 \otimes M_2$ of modules M_1 and M_2 over a Lie group G can be considered as a module over G by defining

$$g\left[\sum_i m_{1i} \otimes m_{2i}\right] = \sum_i (gm_{1i}) \otimes (gm_{2i}).$$

We can pass from modules over Lie groups to modules over Lie algebras by differentiation, or vice versa by exponentiation. To motivate this discussion we shall restrict our attention to linear Lie groups and algebras, that is, groups and algebras whose elements are linear operators in a finite-dimensional vector space. If x is an element of a linear Lie algebra L, then $g = e^{tx} = 1 + tx + \cdots$ is an element of a linear Lie group. For sufficiently small real numbers t, we could ignore higher order terms. Then, inserting this expansion for g in the above definition of its action on the tensor product space, and comparing powers of t, we arrive at the formula

$$x\left[\sum_i m_{1i} \otimes m_{2i}\right] = \sum_i [xm_{1i} \otimes m_{2i} + m_{1i} \otimes xm_{2i}].$$

We may now drop the restriction to linear Lie algebras by using this formula to define tensor products of modules over abstract Lie algebras. If M_1 and M_2 are modules over a Lie algebra L, this formula defines an action of L on the tensor product vector space $M_1 \otimes M_2$ making it into a module over L. It can be verified directly that the axioms for a module over a Lie algebra are satisfied without reference to Lie groups. As a mnemonic aid we may further note that the rule

$$x(m_1 \otimes m_2) = (xm_1) \otimes m_2 + m_1 \otimes (xm_2)$$

may be viewed as an abstract generalization of the Leibniz rule for differentiating a product.

Consider the tensor product of two modules over a Lie algebra. If the Lie algebra is semisimple, then the original two modules are completely reducible, and so can be written as a direct sum of irreducible submodules. The tensor product is then just the direct sum of all the tensor products of these irreducible submodules. To reduce the tensor product of arbitrary modules over a semisimple Lie algebra, therefore, it is sufficient to study the reductions of tensor products of irreducible modules as direct sums of irreducible modules. In the applied literature, these expansions of tensor products of irreducible submodules as direct sums of irreducible submodules are called *Clebsch–Gordan series*. In particular, the Clebsch–Gordan series for the rotation group play a fundamental role in the quantum mechanical description of atomic and nuclear spectroscopy.

Another module operation closely related to the tensor product is the dual operation. The dual vector space M^* consisting of all scalar-valued linear functions on a module M over a Lie algebra L may be considered as a module over L. If the action of L on M^* is defined by

$$(x\phi)(m) = -\phi(xm)$$

for all ϕ in M^* and all m in M, then straightforward computation verifies that M^* satisfies the module axioms. This formula may be understood in terms of the natural pairing of the space M^* with M, that is, the linear mapping of $M^* \otimes M$ into the base field which takes $\phi \otimes m$ to $\phi(m)$ for all ϕ in M^* and all m in M. The definition of the dual module M^* just amounts to the requirement that this natural pairing, or contraction, be a Lie module homomorphism, if we take the base field as a trivial module over L. If a basis $\{e_i\}$ is chosen in M, and the corresponding dual basis $\{e^i\}$ is chosen in M^*, then the representation matrices in the dual module are the negative transposes of the representation matrices in the original module. The action of x on the basis elements e_i can be written as

$$xe_i = \sum_j D^j{}_i(x)e_j.$$

Then, using $(xe^i)(e_j) = -e^i(xe_j)$, a simple computation shows that

$$xe^i = \sum_j \{-D^i{}_j(x)\}e^j.$$

Thus, here $D^j{}_i(x)$ is the matrix representative associated with the module M, and the negative transpose $-D^i{}_j(x)$ gives the corresponding matrix representation associated with the dual module M^*.

2.5 TENSOR AND EXTERIOR ALGEBRAS

Another concept from vector space theory having important applications in the theory of Lie algebras is the tensor algebra of a vector space. Although this algebra is infinite-dimensional, it has extremely simple properties. The tensor algebra is an associative algebra which behaves in many respects like a polynomial algebra except that the tensor algebra is not commutative. For example, each element can be assigned a degree, having the expected properties, and one says that the tensor algebra is a *graded algebra* [56].

We define the tensor algebra by combining the ideas of tensor products and external direct sums. The construction given for the tensor product of two vector spaces can obviously be extended to define a tensor product of any finite number of vector spaces. In particular, the tensor product of V with itself r times, called the *r-th tensor power*,

$$\otimes^r V = V \otimes \cdots \otimes V \quad (r \text{ copies}),$$

is the space of tensors of rank r. Strictly speaking, the tensor products $\otimes^{r+s} V$ and $(\otimes^r V) \otimes (\otimes^s V)$ represent different vector spaces [157], but we shall identify them when we construct the tensor algebra on V. The tensor product of a tensor in $\bigotimes^r V$ and a tensor in $\bigotimes^s V$ may be regarded as a tensor in $\bigotimes^{r+s} V$ by making the natural identification, for instance, of

$$(x_1 \otimes \cdots \otimes x_r) \otimes (y_1 \otimes \cdots \otimes y_s)$$

with

$$x_1 \otimes \cdots \otimes x_r \otimes y_1 \otimes \cdots \otimes y_s.$$

This suggests the idea of forming the *contravariant tensor algebra $T(V)$* on a vector space V over a field $\mathbb{F}$. The tensor algebra is defined as the infinite *weak external direct sum*

$$T(V) = \mathbb{F} \dotplus V \dotplus (V \otimes V) \dotplus \cdots$$

of all the tensor powers of the vector space. The infinite sum here is *weak* in the sense that we consider only finite linear combinations of the elements in the spaces $\mathbb{F}, V, V \otimes V, \cdots$, so that no actual infinite summations ever occur, and no questions of convergence can arise. Being a direct sum of vector spaces, the tensor algebra is clearly a vector space, and with the tensoring together operation $\otimes$ as multiplication, $T(V)$ is an associative algebra with unity. If V is an n-dimensional vector space, then each tensor power $\bigotimes^r V$ has dimension n^r, and hence the tensor algebra $T(V)$ is infinite-dimensional.

Another algebra, closely related to the tensor algebra, is obtained by antisymmetrizing the tensor product. The resulting theory of the exterior algebra provides an elegant way to treat determinants, and has important applications to the theory of Lie groups and Lie algebras. The antisymmetrization process can be effected most quickly by means of a quotient construction as follows.

A *two-sided ideal I* in an associative algebra A is a subspace which satisfies $IA \subset I$ and $AI \subset I$. The *quotient algebra* of an associative algebra A with respect to a two-sided ideal I is the quotient vector space under the multiplication

$$(x + I)(y + I) = (xy) + I.$$

Starting with the tensor algebra $T(V)$ of a vector space V, which is an associative algebra under the $\otimes$ operation, consider the two-sided ideal A generated by all elements of the form $x \otimes x$, where $x \in V$. The quotient algebra

$$E(V) = T(V)/A$$

is an associative algebra with unity called the *exterior algebra* or the *Grassmann algebra* of the vector space V. It is customary to use the symbol $\wedge$ to denote the multiplication operation induced by $\otimes$ in the exterior algebra $E(V)$, so that we have

$$(t_1 + A) \wedge (t_2 + A) = (t_1 \otimes t_2) + A$$

for the cosets of any tensors $t_1, t_2 \in T(V)$. If S_1 and S_2 are any two sub-spaces of the exterior algebra $E(V)$, then $S_1 \wedge S_2$ denotes the subspace of all linear combinations of elements $s_1 \wedge s_2$, where $s_1 \in S_1$ and $s_2 \in S_2$. Since $E(V)$ is an associative algebra, we have

$$S_1 \wedge (S_2 \wedge S_3) = (S_1 \wedge S_2) \wedge S_3$$

for any three subspaces of the exterior algebra. The vector space V is naturally embedded in the exterior algebra $E(V)$, just as it is in the tensor algebra, and we may identify the vector $x \in V$ with the coset $x + A \in E(V)$.

The *exterior power*

$$\wedge^r V = V \wedge \cdots \wedge V \quad (r \text{ copies})$$

is a subspace of the exterior algebra. Elements of the exterior power $\wedge^r V$ are sometimes called *r-vectors*. The whole exterior algebra $E(V)$ is the direct sum of the exterior powers $\wedge^r V$. Thus the exterior algebra can be broken up into pieces each with its own degree, and it is also a graded algebra. The grading of the exterior algebra is directly related to the corresponding grading of the tensor algebra. The ideal A is the direct sum of the individual pieces $A^r = A \cap (\otimes^r V)$ lying in each tensor power, and the quotient space $(\otimes^r V)/A^r$ is naturally isomorphic to the exterior power $\wedge^r V$. The exterior square $V \wedge V$ of a vector space V is a vector space generated by exterior products $x \wedge y$ of vectors x, y in V. If $x \in V$, then

$$x \wedge x = 0,$$

since $x \otimes x$ belongs to the ideal A by definition. If x and y are in V, then

$$(x + y) \wedge (x + y) = 0,$$

and writing this out and using

$$x \wedge x = y \wedge y = 0,$$

we find that

$$x \wedge y = -y \wedge x.$$

Thus, the exterior product $x \wedge y$ of two vectors x and y in V is bilinear in x and y and is antisymmetric under their interchange.

If V is an n-dimensional vector space with basis $e_1, \cdots, e_n$, then the exterior square $V \wedge V$ is a vector space of dimension $\binom{n}{2} = n(n-1)/2$, with basis $e_i \wedge e_j$, where $1 \leq i < j \leq n$. More generally, the products $e_{j_1} \wedge \cdots \wedge e_{j_r}$ with strictly increasing indices $j_1 < \cdots < j_r$ form a basis for the exterior power space $\wedge^r V$ since any change in the order of factors in a product at most changes its sign. If V is an n-dimensional vector space, the exterior power $\wedge^r V$ has dimension $\binom{n}{r} = n!/(r!(n-r)!)$ for $0 \leq r \leq n$ and zero for $r > n$, and hence the exterior algebra $E(V)$ has the finite dimension 2^n.

We now indicate some of the many interesting applications of exterior algebras within vector space theory itself. The vectors $x_1, \cdots, x_r$ are linearly independent if and only if their exterior product

$$x_1 \wedge \cdots \wedge x_r$$

is not zero. Any r-vector of the form

$$x_1 \wedge \cdots \wedge x_r,$$

where $x_1, \cdots, x_r \in V$, is called a *simple r-vector*. If S is an r-dimensional subspace of a vector space V, then there exists a simple r-vector $s \in \wedge^r V$ such that the condition for a vector x to belong to S is $s \wedge x = 0$. If $e_1, \cdots, e_r$ is a basis for the subspace S, then we can take $s = e_1 \wedge \cdots \wedge e_r$.

The exterior square $V \wedge V$ may be identified with the subspace of $V \otimes V$ consisting of all linear combinations of elements of the form

$$x \otimes y - y \otimes x,$$

where x and y are in V. More generally, the exterior power $\wedge^k V$ may be identified with the subspace of $\otimes^k V$ consisting of all linear combinations of elements of the form

$$\sum_\pi \delta_\pi x_{\pi(1)} \otimes \cdots \otimes x_{\pi(k)},$$

where the x_i are vectors in V, and the sum goes over all permutations π of the indices $1, \cdots, k$. The sign factor δ_π here depends on the parity of the permutation. It is $+1$ for even permutations and -1 for odd permutations. If α is a linear mapping from a vector space V_1 into a vector space V_2, then

$$\otimes^r \alpha = \alpha \otimes \cdots \otimes \alpha \quad (r \text{ copies})$$

is a linear mapping from $\otimes^r V_1$ to $\otimes^r V_2$. Since antisymmetric tensors remain antisymmetric under $\otimes^r \alpha$, we obtain an induced linear mapping $\wedge^r \alpha$ from $\wedge^r V_1$ to $\wedge^r V_2$. If V is n-dimensional, then $\wedge^n V$ is one-dimensional. The operator $\wedge^n \alpha$ induced by any linear operator α on V may be identified with the determinant of α. If $e_1, \cdots, e_n$ is a basis for V, then we have, explicitly,

$$(\alpha e_1) \wedge \cdots \wedge (\alpha e_n) = (\det \alpha) e_1 \wedge \cdots \wedge e_n.$$

The exterior powers of a module are essential for the construction of the irreducible modules of certain Lie algebras. It is clear that the tensor power $\otimes^r M$ of a Lie module M is again a module over the Lie algebra L. The subspace A^r, spanned by all elements of the form

$$a \otimes m \otimes m \otimes b,$$

where m is in M and where $a \in \otimes^k M$ and $b \in \otimes^{r-k-2} M$ are tensors of lower rank ($0 \leqq k \leqq r - 2$), is a submodule of the tensor power $\otimes^r M$. To see this, we consider the action of an element x of the Lie algebra on $a \otimes m \otimes m \otimes b$, and use

$$x(m \otimes m) = (m + xm) \otimes (m + xm) - m \otimes m - (xm) \otimes (xm).$$

The exterior power, being the quotient space

$$\wedge^r M = (\bigotimes^r M)/A^r,$$

is, therefore, also a module over the Lie algebra L. The action of an element x of L on the elements of $\wedge^r M$ is induced by the action of x in $\bigotimes^r M$, namely,

$$x(m_1 \wedge \cdots \wedge m_r) = \sum_{i=1}^{r} m_1 \wedge \cdots \wedge (xm_i) \wedge \cdots \wedge m_r.$$

2.6 THE UNIVERSAL ENVELOPING ALGEBRA OF A LIE ALGEBRA

Of central importance in Lie algebra theory is another algebra obtained from a tensor algebra by means of a quotient construction. This associative algebra, called the universal enveloping algebra of a Lie algebra, is important because it allows us to translate questions about Lie algebras into corresponding questions about associative algebras. We have seen that Lie group theory reduces locally to the theory of Lie algebras. By means of the enveloping algebra, the theory of Lie algebras is reduced to the even better understood theory of associative algebras. Homomorphisms of one Lie algebra into another induce corresponding homomorphisms of their universal enveloping algebras. Moreover, the ideal generated in the universal enveloping algebra by the kernel of a Lie algebra homomorphism is the kernel of the induced homomorphism on the corresponding universal enveloping algebras. More generally, Lie subalgebras and Lie algebra ideals yield corresponding associative subalgebras and ideals in the universal enveloping algebra.

Intuitively, the universal enveloping associative algebra $U(L)$ consists of all polynomials in elements of the Lie algebra L and a unity element, with the Lie product $[x, y]$ of elements x and y in L being identified with the commutator $xy - yx$. More formally, we can construct the universal enveloping algebra as follows. Since the Lie algebra L is a vector space, it is possible to construct its contravariant tensor algebra $T(L) = \mathbb{F} \dotplus L \dotplus (L \otimes L) \dotplus \cdots$, as before. In this associative algebra $T(L)$, we consider the two-sided ideal K generated by the set of all elements of the form

$$[x, y] - (x \otimes y - y \otimes x),$$

where x and y are elements of L. The ideal K thus contains the differences between Lie algebra products and the corresponding commutators in the associative tensor algebra. If we consider the associative quotient algebra

$U(L) = T(L)/K$, then Lie products will not be distinguished from. commutators since they belong to the same coset. The associative algebra

$$U(L) = T(L)/K$$

is called the *universal enveloping algebra* of the Lie algebra L. As with any associative algebra, we can also make $U(L)$ a Lie algebra using the commutator operation as the Lie product. If we do this, we can consider L to be injected homomorphically into $U(L)$, considered as a Lie algebra.

The associative algebra $U(L)$ is useful because of the following property. Suppose that A is an arbitrary associative algebra, and that A is also given the commutator Lie algebra structure. Any homomorphism of L into A, considered as a Lie algebra, has a unique extension to an associative algebra homomorphism of $U(L)$ into A. Now a representation of a Lie algebra L is a Lie homomorphism of L into the associative algebra of all linear operators on the module, with the Lie product of two linear operators being their commutator. Thus every representation of a Lie algebra L can be extended to a representation of its universal enveloping associative algebra $U(L)$, and we see that every module over L can also be regarded as a module over its enveloping algebra $U(L)$. This idea is central to certain proofs of complete reducibility for modules over semisimple Lie algebras which are based on the universal enveloping algebra.

The associative algebra $U(L)$ acts on the module M by letting

$$(x_1 \cdots x_n)m = x_1(x_2(\cdots(x_n m)\cdots))$$

for all n, for $x_1, \cdots, x_n$ in L and m in M, and extending the definition to all of $U(L)$. It is easily checked that this definition is independent of the choice of coset representatives and so actually defines an action of $U(L) = T(L)/K$ on M.

The enveloping algebra $U(L)$ has a great deal of structure which we may describe briefly here. If $\{x_i\}$ is a basis for L, then the monomials of the form

$$x_{i_1} \otimes \cdots \otimes x_{i_n}, \qquad\qquad n = 0, 1, 2, \cdots,$$

where we take the trivial monomial 1 in case $n = 0$, span $T(L)$, and hence their cosets span $U(L)$. A result of Poincaré, Birkhoff and Witt is that if we only take monomials having their indices i_j in ascending order, allowing repetition, then the cosets of these monomials, again including 1, form a basis for $U(L)$.

It can be shown that $U(L)$ has no nonzero zero divisors and that, for finite-dimensional L, there cannot be an infinite sequence of ideals or one-sided ideals in $U(L)$ each properly contained in the next. If L is finite-dimensional, then every ideal of $U(L)$ is finitely generated. From this, one can conclude by the Goldie–Ore theorem that $U(L)$ has a (two-sided) division ring of fractions [61], [98], [99], [135]. A division ring D is said to be a *division ring of fractions* for $U(L)$ if $U(L)$ is a subring of D and every element of D can be written as $a^{-1}b$ and cd^{-1}, where a, b, c and d are elements of $U(L)$.

The universal enveloping algebra has still another structure of considerable importance [224]. The tensor product of two associative algebras is an associative algebra under the product

$$(x \otimes y)(x' \otimes y') = xx' \otimes yy'.$$

In particular, then $U(L) \otimes U(L)$ is an associative algebra and the mapping $L \to U(L) \otimes U(L)$ which takes any element $l \in L$ into the element $1 \otimes l + l \otimes 1 \in U(L) \otimes U(L)$ is a Lie algebra homomorphism. This Lie homomorphism can then be extended to an associative algebra homomorphism

$$\delta : U(L) \to U(L) \otimes U(L),$$

which we call the *diagonal mapping*. The multiplication map $A \times A \to A$ for any associative algebra A is a bilinear mapping which can of course be replaced by a linear mapping $A \otimes A \to A$. A linear mapping which goes in the opposite direction, $A \to A \otimes A$, is sometimes called a *comultiplication*, and A may be called in this case a *coalgebra*. Thus we may regard the universal enveloping associative algebra $U(L)$ to be both an algebra and a coalgebra.

2.7 NILPOTENT AND CARTAN SUBALGEBRAS

We now discuss some ideas, many dating back to Cartan, needed to analyze the structure of Lie algebras in more detail [45], [46]. Although these results are mostly important for the structure of simple Lie algebras, it is possible to apply some of these ideas to Lie algebras in general. A Lie algebra L is said to be *nilpotent* if the *lower central series* of ideals

$$L \supset L^2 = [L, L] \supset \cdots \supset L^{k+1} = [L^k, L] \supset \cdots$$

is eventually zero. We must distinguish this sequence of ideals from the derived series of ideals $L^{(k)}$ used in defining solvable Lie algebras. Since it is easy to show that $L^{(k)} \subset L^{2^k}$, it follows that every nilpotent Lie algebra is solvable. On the other hand, the two-dimensional non-Abelian Lie algebra defined by $[e_1, e_2] = e_1$ is solvable, but not nilpotent since L^k is spanned by e_1 for all $k \geq 1$. Nevertheless, solvable Lie algebras are only a little bit more general than nilpotent Lie algebras. A finite-dimensional Lie algebra L is solvable if and only if its derived algebra $[L, L]$ is nilpotent. Engel showed that a Lie algebra is nilpotent if and only if $\text{ad } x$ is a nilpotent linear operator (that is, some power of $\text{ad } x$ vanishes) for every element x in the Lie algebra [133]. More recently, Barnes showed that a finite-dimensional Lie algebra is nilpotent if and only if all its maximal subalgebras are ideals [21]. We now study a certain special type of nilpotent subalgebra called a Cartan subalgebra. The *Fitting null component* L_H^0 of a Lie algebra L with respect to a nilpotent subalgebra H is the subspace of L on which $\text{ad } h$ is nilpotent for all $h \in H$. That is, an element y in L belongs to L_H^0 if for every $h \in H$ there is an integer $n > 0$ such that

$$(\text{ad } h)^n y = 0.$$

Since H is a nilpotent subalgebra of L, Engel's theorem implies that $H \subset L_H^0$. A *Cartan subalgebra H* of a Lie algebra L is a nilpotent subalgebra for which $H = L_H^0$. In other words, a Cartan subalgebra H of a Lie algebra L is a nilpotent subalgebra such that if $x \in L$ satisfies

$$[h, [h, \cdots [h, x] \cdots]] = 0$$

for all h in H, then x is also in H. There is an alternative characterization of a Cartan subalgebra which is occasionally useful. A nilpotent subalgebra H of a Lie algebra L is a Cartan subalgebra if and only if H is not contained as an ideal in any subalgebra of L larger than H itself. Every finite-dimensional Lie algebra contains at least one Cartan subalgebra [23]. In general, a Lie algebra L may have more than one Cartan subalgebra, but they all have the same dimension l, called the *rank* of the Lie algebra L. The Cartan subalgebras of a semisimple Lie algebra are maximal Abelian subalgebras. However, the reader should be warned that the converse is not true. A maximal Abelian subalgebra of a semisimple Lie algebra need not be a Cartan subalgebra.

2.8 WEIGHT SUBMODULES

A useful tool for the classification of modules over semisimple Lie algebras is provided by the concept of a weight. The study of weights also has a practical value for exhibiting the internal structure of a Lie module, enabling one to see what that module contains.

Although the concept of weight is most useful in connection with semisimple complex Lie algebras, we can define weights for a module M over any Lie algebra L. A linear form $\mu \in L^*$ is called a *weight* of M if there exists a nonzero vector v in M such that

$$xv = \mu(x)v.$$

The vector v is thus an eigenvector for all elements of L simultaneously, with $\mu(x)$ being the eigenvalue corresponding to the operator x acting in M. The weight μ may thus be considered as this collection of eigenvalues. Lie proved that if L is a solvable Lie algebra over the complex numbers, then any nonzero module over L has at least one weight. The set of all weights of a module is called its *weight system*. In the case of a single linear operator acting on a finite-dimensional vector space over the complex number field, there is a very detailed structure theory culminating in the Jordan canonical form. In that theory it is necessary to generalize slightly the concept of eigenvectors in order to obtain direct sum decompositions. For nilpotent

Lie algebras over the complex number field we can develop a rather similar albeit less detailed theory. To obtain direct sum decompositions of modules over nilpotent Lie algebras, it is similarly necessary to generalize somewhat the concept of a simultaneous eigenvector.

A nonzero vector v in M is called a *weight vector*, or *generalized simultaneous eigenvector*, if there exists an integer p such that

$$(x - \mu(x)1)^p v = 0$$

for all x in L. The set of all weight vectors corresponding to a given weight μ, together with the zero vector, is a submodule M_L^μ of the module M, called the *weight submodule* for the weight μ. In the weight submodule M_L^μ each element x in L is represented by an operator which differs from a multiple of the unit operator by a nilpotent operator. For a module over a nilpotent Lie algebra we can find a basis consisting entirely of weight vectors. In other words, a module over a nilpotent Lie algebra is the direct sum of its weight submodules.

To apply these ideas to a semisimple complex Lie algebra L, we make use of one of its Cartan subalgebras H. Any module M over the semisimple Lie algebra L is also a module over the Abelian subalgebra H. Any module over a semisimple Lie algebra L can then be written as the direct sum of its weight submodules with respect to H:

$$M = \bigoplus_\mu M_H^\mu.$$

In this particular application, the weight submodules actually contain only ordinary eigenvectors.

2.9 ROOTS OF SEMISIMPLE LIE ALGEBRAS

Let H be a Cartan subalgebra of any Lie algebra L over the complex numbers, and let H^* denote its dual space, that is, the set of all complex-valued linear forms on H. A linear form $\alpha \in H^*$ is called a *root* if there exists a nonzero element $x \in L$ such that

$$[h, x] = \alpha(h)x$$

for all $h \in H$. Roots play the same role for the structure of Lie algebras that weights play for Lie modules. The concept of root is in fact just a special case of the concept of weight which applies to the adjoint representation of the Lie algebra. Thus, regarding L itself as a module over H via the adjoint representation, we obtain a decomposition of L as a direct sum of its *root spaces* L_H^α. The Cartan subalgebra H itself is just the root space for $\alpha = 0$ since $H = L_H^0$.

For semisimple Lie algebras over the complex numbers, the above results may be further sharpened. The restriction of the bilinear Killing form on L to the Cartan subalgebra H is in this case nonsingular. This means that for every linear form $\alpha \in H^*$ there is a unique vector $h_\alpha \in H$ such that

$$(h_\alpha, h) = \alpha(h)$$

for all $h \in H$, and thus we can identify the dual space H^* with H itself. The root system has a number of special properties for semisimple Lie algebras. For example, if α is a nonzero root, so is $-\alpha$, but there are no roots which are multiples of α other than α, 0 and $-\alpha$. Moreover, for semisimple complex Lie algebras, the root spaces L_H^α corresponding to nonzero roots α are all one-dimensional [81]. Thus, for any nonzero root α, there is, up to a factor, a unique vector $e_\alpha \in L$, called a *root vector*, such that

$$[h, e_\alpha] = \alpha(h)e_\alpha$$

for all $h \in H$. In other words, for all h in H, this root vector e_α is a simultaneous eigenvector of the linear operators ad h acting on L.

If e_α and e_β are root vectors, then by the Jacobi identity,

$$[h, [e_\alpha, e_\beta]] = (\alpha(h) + \beta(h))[e_\alpha, e_\beta]$$

for all $h \in H$. If $\alpha + \beta$ is a nonzero root, then it follows that $[e_\alpha, e_\beta]$ is a multiple of $e_{\alpha + \beta}$, while if $\alpha + \beta$ is not a root, then $[e_\alpha, e_\beta] = 0$. Finally, in the case $\alpha + \beta = 0$, we have the formula

$$[e_\alpha, e_{-\alpha}] = (e_\alpha, e_{-\alpha})h_\alpha.$$

A semisimple complex Lie algebra L is the direct sum of the l-dimensional Cartan subalgebra H and all the one-dimensional root spaces L_H^α corresponding to nonzero roots,

$$L = H \oplus \left(\bigoplus_{\alpha \neq 0} L_H^\alpha \right).$$

Thus, a basis for H together with the e_α determines a basis for L. It follows, therefore, that the total number of nonzero roots of a semisimple Lie algebra is equal to its dimension minus its rank. If α and β are roots such that $\alpha + \beta \neq 0$, then the corresponding root vectors e_α and e_β are orthogonal. Hence e_α and $e_{-\alpha}$ are both null vectors, but they are never orthogonal to each other, and hence the bilinear Killing form restricted to the plane spanned by them is nonsingular.

To further study the root system of a complex semisimple Lie algebra, we introduce a certain Euclidean space and an ordering of the roots. Let H_R^* denote the real l-dimensional subspace of H^* whose elements are all real linear combinations of roots. Since H^* can be identified with H, we may define a metric on the dual space H^* by

$$(\alpha, \beta) = (h_\alpha, h_\beta)$$

for all α and β in H^*. If α and β are nonzero roots, then (α, β) is real and (α, α) is positive nonzero. The Killing form is thus positive definite on the real space H_R^*, making this a Euclidean space with the Killing form as inner product. We obtain a total ordering of the roots by choosing an arbitrary ordered basis $\gamma_1, \cdots, \gamma_l$ for the real Euclidean space H_R^*.

If $\xi \in H_R^*$, then

$$\xi = r_1\gamma_1 + \cdots + r_l\gamma_l,$$

where the components $r_1, \cdots, r_l$ of the vector ξ are real numbers. We define a *lexicographic ordering* in H_R^* by saying that a vector ξ is *higher* than a vector η, written $\xi > \eta$, if the first nonzero component of their difference $\xi - \eta$ is positive. A root α is called a *positive root* if $\alpha > 0$, a definition which depends, of course, on which choice of lexicographic ordering is made. A *simple root* is a positive root which is not the sum of two positive roots. There are exactly l simple roots, $\alpha_1, \cdots, \alpha_l$, which form a basis for H^*. Each positive root is a linear combination with nonnegative integer coefficients of the simple roots, and each negative root is such a combination with nonpositive integer coefficients. Thus, for any root α, we may write

$$\alpha = k_1\alpha_1 + \cdots + k_l\alpha_l,$$

where the integers $k_1, \cdots, k_l$ have the same sign; if $\alpha > 0$, then $k_1 \geq 0, \cdots,$ $k_l \geq 0$, while if $\alpha < 0$, then $k_1 \leq 0, \cdots, k_l \leq 0$. The sum $k_1 + \cdots + k_l$, called the *level* of the root α, is positive for $\alpha > 0$, zero for $\alpha = 0$, and negative for $\alpha < 0$.

A simple and useful property of weights and roots is their additivity with respect to taking tensor products. If M_H^μ and N_H^ν are weight submodules of the modules M and N over a nilpotent Lie algebra H, then the tensor product $M_H^\mu \otimes N_H^\nu$ is contained in the weight submodule $(M \otimes N)_H^{\mu+\nu}$ of the module $M \otimes N$. There are vectors v and w in M_H^μ and N_H^ν, respectively, such that

$$hv = \mu(h)v \quad \text{and} \quad hw = \nu(h)w$$

for all $h \in H$, and hence,

$$h(v \otimes w) = (hv) \otimes w + v \otimes (hw)$$

$$= (\mu(h) + \nu(h))(v \otimes w).$$

Thus, $\mu + \nu$ is one of the weights in the tensor product of these weight submodules, and in fact it is the only weight in this tensor product.

In general, the weight system of the tensor product $M \otimes N$ of any two modules M and N is the collection of sums of a weight of M and a weight of N. That is, the weight system of a tensor product of two modules can be obtained from the weight systems of the two individual modules by a process of vector addition. These results can be used as follows to clarify the action of a Lie algebra L on one of its modules M. This action $L \times M \to M$ can be formally identified with a module homomorphism $L \otimes M \to M$ by using the tensor product lifting property. It follows that the action of a root subspace L_H^α on a weight submodule M_H^μ is given by the shifting rule $L_H^\alpha M_H^\mu \subset M_H^{\mu+\alpha}$. This shifting rule says that if a root vector e_α acts on a weight vector v with weight μ, then $e_\alpha v$ is either zero, or else a weight vector corresponding to the shifted weight $\mu + \alpha$. We have in fact already met one special case of this shifting rule before, namely,

$$[L_H^\alpha, L_H^\beta] \subset L_H^{\alpha+\beta},$$

which we proved directly, using the Jacobi identity.

Suppose now that M is a module over a semisimple Lie algebra L. Acting on a weight submodule M_H^μ repeatedly with e_α and $e_{-\alpha}$, we get weight submodules corresponding to a whole *ladder of weights* $\mu + z\alpha$, where $z = 0, \pm 1, \pm 2, \cdots$. Since we are dealing with finite-dimensional modules, all but finitely many of the weight modules corresponding to the infinite weight ladder are trivial, and we really only need to consider a finite set $\mu - p\alpha, \cdots, \mu + q\alpha$. The study of these ladders of weights is important for the structure theory of modules over semisimple Lie algebras. The direct sum of the corresponding weight modules, which we may call a *weight-ladder module*, can be regarded as a module over the *ladder-generating Lie sub-algebra* $H \oplus L_H^\alpha \oplus L_H^{-\alpha}$.

2.10 THE FACTORIZATION METHOD AND SPECIAL FUNCTIONS

The value of the concepts of roots and weights is not limited to semi-simple Lie algebras. One example of the use of these concepts in a more general setting arises in the theory of the special functions of mathematical physics. In addition to the elementary transcendental functions, such as e^x and $\sin x$, these special functions include the Bessel functions, Legendre polynomials, parabolic cylinder functions, Hermite polynomials and so forth. Many of them share a variety of interesting properties, such as recurrence relations, addition theorems, generating functions, orthogonality relations, integral representations and so on. A partial explanation of these regularities lies in the fact that many of these functions may be regarded as special cases of the ordinary or confluent hypergeometric functions. A deeper reason, perhaps, is that many of these functions arise from the solution of the Laplace equation upon separating variables. In general, special functions arising from the solution of the Laplace equation or its generalizations are called *harmonic functions* or *spherical functions* [102], [162], [232]. Now, the Laplace equation is an example of a differential equation invariant under the action of a certain Lie group. Hence, it is reasonable to suppose that the theory of special functions can be unified and also generalized by making use of ideas from the theory of Lie groups and Lie algebras [225], [234]. An obvious generalization, for example, would be to replace the Laplace operator for flat Euclidean space $\mathbb{R}^n$ by an analogous operator for a curved symmetric space such as a sphere [243].

One important method for studying special functions via their recursion relations, known as the *factorization method*, ties in closely with the standard Lie algebraic techniques involving roots and weights. Infield and Hull gave a systematic catalogue of the special functions which can be studied by this method, which involves factorizing the appropriate second order differential equation [128]. For the Hermite polynomials, which are related to the harmonic oscillator, this leads to the creation and annihilation operators considered previously. Hull and Infield reduced the entire list of possibilities to six overlapping classes, later shown by Miller to arise naturally in the representation theory of four particular Lie algebras [168], [169]. These include the Lie algebras of the three-dimensional rotation group and the groups of Euclidean motions in a plane and in space, as well as a certain four-dimensional solvable Lie algebra. The Lie algebras that one studies are those generated by the differential operators which figure in the recursion relations. The recursion relations for the special functions themselves can be viewed as examples of the shifting rule for root vectors acting on weight vectors.

As an example, we discuss the Bessel functions, which are related to the three-dimensional Lie algebra of the group of Euclidean motions in a plane [233], [248]. Any Euclidean motion in the plane can be composed out of a translation and a rotation about the origin. The angle ϕ of the rotation and the orthogonal components (x, y) of the translation may serve as local coordinates for a neighborhood of the identity in the Euclidean group of a plane. We denote by $\mathbf{T}_x$, $\mathbf{T}_y$ and $\mathbf{M}$ tangent vectors corresponding to the one-parameter subgroups consisting, respectively, of translations in the x direction and y direction, and rotations about the origin. We can identify the basis vectors $\mathbf{T}_x$, $\mathbf{T}_y$ and $\mathbf{M}$ for the Lie algebra with differential operators:

$$\mathbf{T}_x \mapsto \frac{\partial}{\partial x}, \quad \mathbf{T}_y \mapsto \frac{\partial}{\partial y}, \quad \mathbf{M} \mapsto \frac{\partial}{\partial \phi} = x\frac{\partial}{\partial y} - y\frac{\partial}{\partial x}.$$

This yields an isomorphism of the Lie algebra of the plane Euclidean group with a Lie algebra of differential operators on the infinitely differentiable functions on the plane, the Lie product being commutation. Note that the element

$$\mathbf{T}_x^2 + \mathbf{T}_y^2$$

in the enveloping algebra of the Euclidean Lie algebra corresponds to the Laplacian operator in the (x, y)-plane,

$$\nabla^2 = \frac{\partial^2}{\partial x^2} + \frac{\partial^2}{\partial y^2}.$$

An element of the universal enveloping algebra, such as $T_x^2 + T_y^2$, which commutes with the whole Lie algebra is called a *Casimir element*. In any module, the eigenspaces of a Casimir element are submodules, and hence such an element can have only one eigenvalue in an irreducible module. For our purposes, it will be sufficient to study one such irreducible module, consisting of eigenvectors of ∇^2 with eigenvalue -1. A set of solutions for the corresponding differential equation

$$(\nabla^2 + 1)\psi_m = 0$$

is given by the functions

$$\psi_m(r, \phi) = e^{im\phi} J_m(r),$$

by using polar coordinates (r, ϕ) in the (x, y)-plane. In fact, it is easy to transform this equation into the standard differential equation for the Bessel function $J_m(r)$. The complexification of the real Lie algebra of the plane Euclidean group is not semisimple since the subspace spanned by T_x and T_y is an Abelian ideal. This Lie algebra is in fact an example of a solvable Lie algebra which is not nilpotent.

The line spanned by M and the plane spanned by T_x and T_y are both maximal Abelian subalgebras. However, only the line spanned by M is a Cartan subalgebra, while the plane spanned by T_x and T_y is not. By setting

$$T_\pm = T_x \pm iT_y,$$

the commutation relations take on the simple form

$$[T_+, T_-] = 0, \qquad [M, T_\pm] = \pm iT_\pm.$$

Thus, taking the line spanned by M as our Cartan subalgebra, we may interpret the three lines spanned respectively by M, T_+ and T_- as root spaces. Note that the Laplacian operator factorizes in terms of T_+ and T_-,

$$T_+ T_- = T_- T_+ \mapsto \nabla^2.$$

Since $M\psi_m = im\psi_m$, the vector ψ_m is an eigenvector of M, and hence spans a weight submodule. The elements T_+ and T_- act as raising and lowering elements, satisfying the shifting rule

$$T_\pm \psi_m = \mp \psi_{m\pm 1}.$$

To interpret this formula we use

$$T_\pm \mapsto \frac{\partial}{\partial x} \pm i\frac{\partial}{\partial y} = e^{\pm i\phi}\left(\frac{\partial}{\partial r} \pm \frac{i}{r}\frac{\partial}{\partial \phi}\right).$$

The shifting rule then reduces to the usual recursion relation for Bessel functions,

$$r\frac{d}{dr}J_m(r) = \pm(mJ_m(r) - rJ_{m\pm 1}(r)).$$

Many other properties of Bessel functions can be obtained by means of the Lie algebra; for example, addition formulas can be obtained by using the Baker–Hausdorff formulas. Weisner has also obtained generating functions for certain types of special functions using Lie algebraic ideas [237].

2.11 THE CARTAN MATRIX

The structure of a semisimple Lie algebra of rank l is determined up to isomorphism by its system of roots. As a matter of fact, it is even sufficient to know the system of simple roots $\alpha_1, \cdots, \alpha_l$ with respect to some lexicographic ordering of the roots. The *Cartan matrix* $[A_{ij}]$ defined by

$$A_{ij} = \frac{2(\alpha_i, \alpha_j)}{(\alpha_i, \alpha_i)}$$

is important in determining the structure of a semisimple Lie algebra.

If α and β are roots, then the sequence of linear forms

$$\beta - p\alpha, \cdots, \beta - \alpha, \beta, \beta + \alpha, \cdots, \beta + q\alpha$$

is called an α-*ladder through* β if they are all roots and if $\beta - (p + 1)\alpha$ and $\beta + (q + 1)\alpha$ are not roots. Then p and q are related by

$$p - q = 2(\alpha, \beta)/(\alpha, \alpha).$$

It follows from the definition of simple roots that the difference $\alpha - \beta$ between any two distinct simple roots α and β cannot be a root. Hence, if α and β are simple roots, then $p = 0$, and the Cartan matrix determines the α-ladder through the root β. From a knowledge of the Cartan matrix we can determine by an algorithm (using induction on the level of the root β) whether or not a given linear combination of simple roots $\beta = \sum_{i=1}^{l} k_i \alpha_i$ is a positive root. Thus the full root system is determined by the Cartan matrix. Actually, at this point it suffices to know that the Cartan matrix determines the highest root, because the entire root system can be recovered from a knowledge of the highest root. We later describe a more general algorithm due to Dynkin which allows one to compute the weight system of any irreducible module from a knowledge of the highest weight.

The Cartan matrix also determines the Lie products, and hence the complete structure of a semisimple Lie algebra. Each simple root corresponds to a certain element

$$h_i = 2h_{\alpha_i}/(\alpha_i, \alpha_i)$$

in the Cartan subalgebra. The normalization was chosen to simplify later computations. The elements $h_1, \cdots, h_l$ form a basis for the chosen Cartan subalgebra of the semisimple Lie algebra. Let the root vector corresponding to a simple root α_i be denoted by

$$e_i = e_{\alpha_i},$$

and let us also define

$$f_i = \frac{2e_{-\alpha_i}}{(\alpha_i, \alpha_i)(e_{\alpha_i}, e_{-\alpha_i})}.$$

The vectors $e_1, \cdots, e_l$, called *simple raising elements*, and the vectors $f_1, \cdots, f_l$, called *simple lowering elements*, together generate the whole Lie algebra. The Lie products are given by

$$[h_i, h_j] = 0, \qquad\qquad [h_i, e_j] = A_{ij}e_j,$$

$$[h_i, f_j] = -A_{ij}f_j, \qquad [e_i, f_j] = \delta_{ij}h_i.$$

We caution the reader that in these formulas one does not sum over the repeated indices.

The relations written above do not yet completely define all products, for $[e_i, e_j]$ and $[f_i, f_j]$ have not been specified. The complete set of relations can nevertheless be derived from the above set by a well-defined algorithm which we shall shortly illustrate in a special case. The elements h_i, together with

$$e_{i_1 \cdots i_s} = [e_{i_1}, \cdots [e_{i_{s-1}}, e_{i_s}] \cdots]$$

and

$$f_{i_1 \cdots i_s} = [f_{i_1}, \cdots [f_{i_{s-1}}, f_{i_s}] \cdots],$$

span the Lie algebra. All linear relations and commutation relations for these elements are computable from the Cartan matrix.

2.12 THE WEYL GROUP

The roots of a semisimple Lie algebra and the weights of any of its modules are vectors lying in the dual space H^* of a Cartan subalgebra H. Moreover, these weights, just as the roots, are rational linear combinations of the simple roots $\alpha_1, \cdots, \alpha_l$. Hence the weight system of any module over a semisimple Lie algebra of rank l is a set of points lying in the l-dimensional real Euclidean space H_R^* of all real linear combinations of the simple roots. Since this Euclidean space is lexicographically ordered with respect to an arbitrary basis, we may regard the weights of a module as a totally ordered set. For a finite-dimensional module, there are only a finite number of different weights, and hence there must be a *highest weight* which is higher than all the others. Two irreducible modules over a semisimple Lie algebra are isomorphic if and only if their highest weights are equal. Thus the irreducible modules over a semisimple Lie algebra are characterized by their highest weights.

To study the structure of an irreducible module with a given highest weight λ, we must have a way of calculating its weight system. The weight system has certain symmetry properties which we now study. If μ is a weight and if α is a nonzero root, then there is a ladder of weights

$$\mu - p\alpha, \cdots, \mu + q\alpha$$

which also belongs to the weight system. The real number

$$n = 2(\mu, \alpha)/(\alpha, \alpha)$$

is an integer, and $\mu - n\alpha$ is one of the weights in this ladder. This transformation may be interpreted geometrically as a reflection w_α in the plane perpendicular to the root α in H_R^*. These reflections are called *Weyl reflections*, and the group generated by them is called the *Weyl group* of the Lie algebra. It is clear that the Weyl reflections must satisfy

$$w_\alpha^2 = 1 \quad \text{and} \quad w_{-\alpha} = w_\alpha.$$

The weight system of any module is invariant under the Weyl group. The Killing form also is invariant under the Weyl group. If w is any element of the Weyl group W, then

$$(w\alpha, w\beta) = (\alpha, \beta).$$

In general, the root system may have a higher degree of symmetry than some of the other weight systems. This is because the root system is not only invariant under the Weyl group, but also under the inversion $\alpha \mapsto -\alpha$. The sets of vectors which can represent root systems of semisimple Lie algebras are restricted by the following three conditions:

1. If α is a root, then $-\alpha$ is a root, but no other nonzero multiples of α are roots.
2. If α and β are nonzero roots, then

$$2(\alpha, \beta)/(\alpha, \alpha)$$

is 0, ± 1, ± 2 or ± 3.
3. The Weyl reflection of a root β in the hyperplane through the origin perpendicular to any nonzero root α yields another root,

$$\beta - 2\frac{(\beta, \alpha)}{(\alpha, \alpha)}\alpha.$$

From these three properties of the root system, one can deduce a number of other simple properties. For example, it follows that the angle between any two nonzero roots can only be $0°$, $30°$, $45°$, $60°$, $90°$, $120°$, $135°$, $150°$ or $180°$. Also, the relative lengths of any two nonzero and nonorthogonal roots are determined by the angle between them. If this angle is $0°$, $60°$, $120°$ or $180°$, then the roots are of equal length. If the angle is $45°$ or $135°$, their relative lengths are in the ratio $\sqrt{2}:1$, while if the angle is $30°$ or $150°$, then this ratio is $\sqrt{3}:1$. In fact, these three conditions alone determine the possible root systems, and hence all the possible semisimple Lie algebras over the complex numbers.

2.13 DYNKIN DIAGRAMS

While the problem of finding all semisimple complex Lie algebras has thus been reduced to a geometrical problem, Dynkin found an even simpler way of doing this by using diagrams in a plane [81]. He represents a system of simple roots $\alpha_1, \cdots, \alpha_l$ by a set of l points in a plane, where l is the rank of the Lie algebra. These points form the vertices of the *Dynkin diagram*. The points representing α_i and α_j are connected by

$$A_{ij}A_{ji} = \frac{4(\alpha_i, \alpha_j)^2}{(\alpha_i, \alpha_i)(\alpha_j, \alpha_j)} = 4\cos^2 \sphericalangle\, \alpha_i, \alpha_j$$

lines. The number of lines determines the angle between the roots, since $(\alpha_i, \alpha_j) \leq 0$ for simple roots. Thus the angle $\sphericalangle\, \alpha_i, \alpha_j$ is respectively 90°, 120°, 135° or 150° if the number of lines which connect the ith and jth vertices is zero, one, two or three. While the Dynkin diagram of a simple Lie algebra is connected, the Dynkin diagram of a semisimple Lie algebra which is not simple is not connected. The connected components of the Dynkin diagram of a semisimple Lie algebra correspond to the simple ideals occurring in a direct sum decomposition of the Lie algebra.

The relative lengths of the simple roots are indicated in the Dynkin diagram by using light and dark circles to represent the vertices. If all roots are of the same length, all the circles are light. For simple Lie algebras, the only other possibility is that there are roots of two different lengths. The long roots are then assigned light circles, the short roots dark circles. The Dynkin diagram thus allows one to compute the angles between the simple roots and their relative lengths. The absolute lengths of the roots may be obtained from an observation of Brown that the sum of the squares of the lengths of all the roots of a semisimple Lie algebra is equal to its rank [41]. From this information one can then draw the root system as a set of points in l-dimensional Euclidean space. The ratios of the square of the lengths of the simple roots are related to the Cartan matrix by

$$\frac{(\alpha_i, \alpha_i)}{(\alpha_j, \alpha_j)} = \frac{A_{ji}}{A_{ij}}.$$

Since the product $A_{ij}A_{ji}$ and the ratio A_{ij}/A_{ji} can be determined from the Dynkin diagrams, we can obviously calculate all the A_{ij}, at least up to signs. The sign is always minus for nonzero off-diagonal elements, and the diagonal elements are clearly $A_{ii} = +2$. Thus the Dynkin diagram determines the Cartan matrix uniquely. From a knowledge of the Dynkin diagram one can therefore reconstruct the Lie algebra, so that the Dynkin diagram completely characterizes a given semisimple Lie algebra.

The three conditions which characterize root systems can be reinterpreted as various restrictions on the possible Dynkin diagrams of simple

Lie algebras. For example, a Dynkin diagram cannot contain any loops, and the total number of lines incident on a given vertex can be at most three. Continuing in this fashion, we can narrow down the possible connected Dynkin diagrams to four general classes and five exceptions. Dynkin diagrams of the four main classes of simple Lie algebras are shown in Fig. 1, while those of the five exceptional simple Lie algebras are shown in Fig. 2.

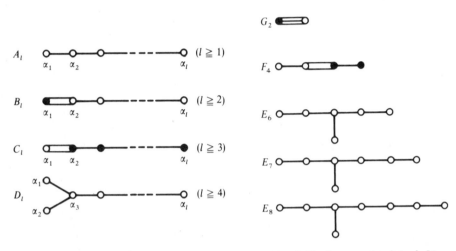

FIG. 1. *The four main classes of simple Lie algebras*

FIG. 2. *The five exceptional simple Lie algebras*

These diagrams represent the only possible simple Lie algebras of finite dimension over the complex number field. Each of these possibilities is actually realized by a Lie algebra which can be explicitly constructed from the diagram.

Another useful application of the Dynkin diagram of a semisimple Lie algebra is found in the description of the structure of the Weyl group. In fact, the Dynkin diagrams are Coxeter diagrams with additional information about root lengths. Coxeter initially introduced these diagrams to study arbitrary reflection groups [67], [68].

The Weyl reflections $w_i = w_{\alpha_i}$ corresponding to the simple roots $\alpha_1, \cdots,$ α_l of a semisimple Lie algebra L, called *simple Weyl reflections*, are a set of generators for the Weyl group of L. These generators satisfy the relations

$$(w_i w_j)^{p_{ij}} = 1,$$

where p_{ij} is 1 if $i = j$, and is 2, 3, 4 or 6 if $i \neq j$ and the ith and jth vertices of the Dynkin diagram are joined by 0, 1, 2 or 3 lines, respectively [47], [209]. The elements of the Weyl group can be generated on a computer using a program depending upon this presentation in terms of generators and relations [24]. This program is based on the observation that S_l, the symmetric group on l letters, is a subgroup of the Weyl group of a simple Lie algebra of rank l. The computer generates S_l recursively and then generates the coset representatives of S_l in the Weyl group.

2.14 IDENTIFICATION OF SIMPLE LIE ALGEBRAS

The four main classes of Dynkin diagrams correspond to simple Lie algebras A_l, B_l, C_l and D_l over the complex numbers which are related to various classical Lie groups. More precisely, we can identify these complex Lie algebras with the complexifications of real Lie algebras of certain compact Lie groups. Thus, for example, the complex Lie algebra A_l is the complexification of the real Lie algebra of the compact special unitary group $SU(l + 1)$. Similarly, the Lie algebras B_l and D_l correspond to the compact rotation groups $SO(2l + 1, \mathbb{R})$ and $SO(2l, \mathbb{R})$, respectively, while C_l corresponds to the unitary symplectic group $Sp(l)$. We can also obtain a direct relation between these complex Lie algebras and the classical groups without complexification by generalizing the discussion of tangent spaces. Just as we obtain real Lie algebras as tangent spaces to groups which are real analytic manifolds, we may obtain complex Lie algebras as tangent spaces to groups which are complex analytic manifolds. We may then identify A_l as the complex Lie algebra of the complex special linear group $SL(l + 1, \mathbb{C})$ if the latter is regarded as a complex analytic group. Similarly, the complex Lie algebras B_l and D_l are related, respectively, to the complex orthogonal groups $SO(2l + 1, \mathbb{C})$ and $SO(2l, \mathbb{C})$, regarding these as complex analytic groups. Finally, the complex Lie algebras C_l correspond to the complex symplectic group $Sp(l, \mathbb{C})$, leaving invariant a nonsingular antisymmetric bilinear form in a complex vector space of dimension $2l$. All of these Lie algebras, which are defined for all $l \geq 1$, are simple Lie algebras except for D_1 and D_2. The algebra D_1 is Abelian, and is thus not simple, while the algebra D_2 is semisimple, and can be identified with $A_1 \dotplus A_1$. For the low-rank Lie algebras there are a number of isomorphisms,

$$A_1 \approx B_1 \approx C_1,$$

$$B_2 \approx C_2,$$

$$A_3 \approx D_3.$$

The dimensions of the main-series complex simple Lie algebras are given by

$$\dim A_l = l(l + 2),$$

$$\dim B_l = l(2l + 1),$$

$$\dim C_l = l(2l + 1),$$

$$\dim D_l = l(2l - 1).$$

The five exceptional simple Lie algebras G_2, F_4, E_6, E_7 and E_8 over the complex numbers can be associated in various ways with the Cayley numbers. These algebras have dimensions 14, 52, 78, 133 and 248, respectively. The exceptional algebra G_2 has been applied by Racah to a problem in atomic spectroscopy [194].

2.15 CONSTRUCTION OF THE LIE ALGEBRA A_2

To illustrate the procedure for determining the structure constants of a simple Lie algebra from its Dynkin diagram, we consider the simple Lie algebra A_2. The Dynkin diagram for the simple Lie algebra A_2 is shown in Fig. 3.

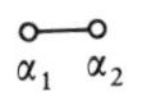

$$\underset{\alpha_1 \ \ \alpha_2}{\circ\!\!-\!\!\circ}$$

Fig. 3. *Dynkin diagram for A_2*

The two simple roots α_1 and α_2 are of equal length, and form an angle of 120°. Hence the Cartan matrix, with components A_{ij}, of the Lie algebra A_2 is

$$\begin{bmatrix} 2 & -1 \\ -1 & 2 \end{bmatrix}.$$

Since the difference of two simple roots obviously cannot be a root, we have $p = 0$ for the α_1-ladder through α_2, and hence,

$$q = -(p - q) = -A_{12} = 1,$$

and this ladder is thus composed of the roots α_2 and $\alpha_1 + \alpha_2$. By considering further ladders, we obtain no more positive roots, and we see that $\alpha_1 + \alpha_2$ is the highest root. Thus the root system of the simple Lie algebra A_2 consists of zero, the positive roots α_1, α_2 and $\alpha_1 + \alpha_2$ and the negative roots $-\alpha_1, -\alpha_2$ and $-(\alpha_1 + \alpha_2)$. The Euclidean space H_R^* spanned by the simple roots α_1 and α_2 is a plane, and thus we can draw the root diagram of the Lie algebra A_2, as shown in Fig. 4.

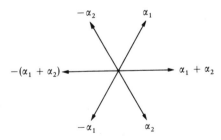

Fig. 4. *Root diagram for A_2*

From this figure it is seen that the root system of A_2 is not only symmetric under the Weyl group, but also possesses an additional symmetry under inversion in the origin.

We obtain part of a canonical basis for A_2 by considering the elements h_1, h_2 and the simple raising and lowering elements e_1, e_2 and f_1, f_2. Their commutation relations are

$$[h_1, e_1] = 2e_1, \quad [h_1, f_1] = -2f_1, \quad [h_2, e_1] = -e_1, \quad [h_2, f_1] = f_1,$$

$$[h_1, e_2] = -e_2, \quad [h_1, f_2] = f_2, \quad [h_2, e_2] = 2e_2, \quad [h_2, f_2] = -2f_2,$$

$$[e_1, f_1] = h_1, \quad [e_2, f_1] = 0, \quad [e_1, f_2] = 0, \quad [e_2, f_2] = h_2$$

and, of course,

$$[h_i, h_j] = 0.$$

We supplement these six elements with the two further elements

$$e_{12} = [e_1, e_2] \quad \text{and} f_{12} = [f_1, f_2],$$

which are root vectors corresponding to the roots $\pm(\alpha_1 + \alpha_2)$, to obtain a total of eight vectors which form a basis for A_2.

The commutation relations involving the elements e_{12} and f_{12} are obtained by using the Jacobi identity, for example,

$$[h_1, e_{12}] = [h_1, [e_1, e_2]] = [[h_1, e_1], e_2] + [e_1, [h_1, e_2]] = 2e_{12} - e_{12} = e_{12}.$$

In this fashion we obtain the following further commutation relations:

$$[h_1, e_{12}] = e_{12}, \quad [h_1, f_{12}] = -f_{12}, \quad [h_2, e_{12}] = e_{12}, \quad [h_2, f_{12}] = -f_{12},$$

$$[e_1, e_{12}] = 0, \quad [e_1, f_{12}] = f_2, \quad [e_2, e_{12}] = 0, \quad [e_2, f_{12}] = -f_1,$$

$$[f_1, e_{12}] = e_2, \quad [f_1, f_{12}] = 0, \quad [f_2, e_{12}] = -e_1, \quad [f_2, f_{12}] = 0,$$

$$[e_{12}, f_{12}] = -(h_1 + h_2).$$

Thus, starting from the Dynkin diagram for A_2 we have completely determined the products of the members of a basis, and hence determined the structure of the Lie algebra. A similar procedure can be carried through to construct the Lie algebra corresponding to any Dynkin diagram.

2.16 COMPLEXIFICATION AND REAL FORMS

We recall that there are four general series of simple Lie algebras over the complex numbers, A_l, B_l, C_l and D_l, and five exceptional simple Lie algebras, G_2, F_4, E_6, E_7 and E_8. Of course, for $l < 4$, some of the general sequence Lie algebras are not defined or they collapse into one another, so we have only A_1, A_2, B_2, A_3, B_3 and C_3. Real simple Lie algebras, such as the algebra $so(3, \mathbb{R})$, are also useful for many applications. The problem of classifying the real simple Lie algebras is only slightly more complicated than classifying the complex ones. This is because the process of complexification relates the real case to the complex case. Hence, we may study the real simple Lie algebras by generating them from the complex algebras. Since a single complex simple Lie algebra in general yields several real ones, we must supplement our study of Dynkin diagrams with further considerations [93], [94].

We recall that the complexification of a real Lie algebra is obtained by tensoring it with the complex number field $\mathbb{C}$ regarded as a vector space over the real numbers. Conversely, we obtain the real restriction L^R of a complex Lie algebra L by simply regarding L itself as an algebra over the real subfield of the complex number field. Note that the processes of complexification and real restriction are not inverses of each other. The complexification of the real restriction of a complex Lie algebra L does not yield back L, but rather $\mathbb{C} \otimes L^R \approx L \dotplus L$.

If we can write the real restriction L^R of a complex Lie algebra L as a direct sum $L_0 \oplus iL_0$ for some real subalgebra L_0, then we call L_0 a *real form* of L. If L_0 is a real form of a complex Lie algebra L, then conversely, L is isomorphic to the complexification of L_0.

Every real simple Lie algebra is either the real restriction or else a real form of a complex simple Lie algebra. The complication of the classification problem for real simple Lie algebras arises from the fact that a complex simple Lie algebra may have several distinct real forms. Or, putting it another way, several different real simple Lie algebras may have isomorphic complexifications. Consider for instance the real Lie algebra $so(3, \mathbb{R})$ of the rotation group and the algebra $so(2, 1; \mathbb{R})$ of the plane Lorentz group, that is, the group of linear transformations on x, y and t leaving $x^2 + y^2 - t^2$ invariant. These real Lie algebras are not isomorphic, but they have isomorphic complexifications, namely the complex simple Lie algebra A_1.

Of all the real forms of a given complex simple Lie algebra, there is precisely one, called the *compact real form*, which is the real Lie algebra of a compact Lie group. In general, a *compact real Lie algebra* is defined to be a real Lie algebra obtained from some compact Lie group. A useful characterization of compact semisimple Lie algebras arises from the fact that a real semisimple Lie algebra is compact if and only if its bilinear Killing form is negative definite. All noncompact real forms of a simple complex Lie algebra can be obtained from the compact one [178], [206]. A detailed list of the real simple Lie algebras, together with their isomorphisms, was found by Cartan [46], [120].

Any real form L_0 of a complex Lie algebra L may of course be regarded as a subalgebra of the real restriction L^R. If $e_1, \cdots, e_n$ are a basis over the real numbers for the real form L_0, then these same vectors are a basis for L over the complex numbers. Moreover, the vectors $e_1, \cdots, e_n, ie_1, \cdots, ie_n$ are linearly independent over the real numbers, and are a basis for the real Lie algebra L^R. We may regard i as a real linear operator on L^R having the properties

$$i^2 = -1 \quad \text{and} \quad [x, iy] = i[x, y]$$

for all x and y in L^R. Any vector $z \in L^R$ may be uniquely written as

$$z = x + iy,$$

where x and y are elements of L_0. We may define an automorphism S of the real Lie algebra L^R by

$$S(x + iy) = x - iy$$

for all x and y in L_0. This is an *involutive automorphism*; that is, S is an automorphism whose square is the identity operator, $S^2 = 1$. Moreover, the operator S is the identity when restricted to L_0, and its negative when restricted to the subspace iL_0. Thus the real form L_0 is the eigenspace of the linear operator S corresponding to the eigenvalue $+1$, while iL_0 is the eigenspace corresponding to the eigenvalue -1.

The compact real form of a complex simple Lie algebra L of rank l can be explicitly constructed as follows. We recall that there is a basis for L consisting of a basis $h_1, \cdots, h_l$ for a Cartan subalgebra H together with root vectors e_α and $e_{-\alpha}$, where α ranges over all the positive roots. It is convenient to normalize these root vectors so that

$$(e_\alpha, e_{-\alpha}) = 2.$$

The vectors $ih_1, \cdots, ih_l$, together with $i(e_\alpha + e_{-\alpha})$ and $e_\alpha - e_{-\alpha}$ for all $\alpha > 0$, then form a basis over the real numbers for the compact real form L_0 of the complex simple Lie algebra L. This particular choice of basis makes it easy to show that the Killing form is negative definite on the compact real form L_0.

Any involutive automorphism S_0 of the compact real form L_0 of a complex simple Lie algebra L can be extended to an automorphism of the real Lie algebra

$$L^R = L_0 \oplus iL_0$$

by defining

$$S(x + iy) = S_0(x) - iS_0(y)$$

for all x and y in L_0. Denoting the eigenspaces of S_0 corresponding to the eigenvalues $+1$ and -1 by L_0^+ and L_0^-, respectively, we obtain the *Cartan decomposition*

$$L_0 = L_0^+ \oplus L_0^-$$

of the compact real form L_0 with respect to S_0. We then find that the vectors of

$$L_1 = L_0^+ \oplus iL_0^-$$

are left fixed by S, while those of iL_1 are carried to their negatives. To show that S is an involutive automorphism of

$$L^R = L_1 \oplus iL_1,$$

we use the fact that S_0 is an automorphism of L_0, so that

$$S_0([x, y]) = [S_0(x), S_0(y)]$$

for all x and y in L_0. Since L_1 consists of all vectors left fixed by S, we see that if x and y are in L_1, then so is $[x, y]$, for we have

$$S([x, y]) = [S(x), S(y)] = [x, y].$$

Hence, $L_1 = L_0^+ \oplus iL_0^-$ is a subalgebra of L^R, and thus it is a real form of the complex Lie algebra L. The subspace L_0^+ is called the *toroidal part* of the real form L_1, while the subspace iL_0^- is called its *vector part*. Since every real form of L induces an involutive automorphism having the properties we required of S_0 on L_0, every real form of L can be obtained in this manner from some automorphism S_0 of the compact real form L_0.

2.17   REAL FORMS OF THE LIE ALGEBRA A_1

The processes of complexification and finding real forms can best be illustrated by means of a simple example. For this purpose we shall con-sider the real Lie algebra $su(2) \approx so(3, \mathbb{R})$ of the ordinary rotation group. We recall again that this Lie algebra is just a real three-dimensional space with the usual vector cross product as multiplication. We can take as a basis a set of elements e_1, e_2 and e_3 with the Lie product given by

$$[e_1, e_2] = e_3, \quad [e_2, e_3] = e_1 \quad \text{and} \quad [e_3, e_1] = e_2.$$

The complexification of $su(2)$ then has the same basis and same Lie products over the complex numbers, this complex Lie algebra being, of course, the complex simple Lie algebra A_1. For the benefit of physicists we remark that it is really this complex Lie algebra A_1 which is usually studied in the quan-tum theory of angular momentum. In angular momentum theory it is conventional not to use the basis elements e_1, e_2, e_3, but to replace them with an obviously equivalent set

$$j_1 = ie_1, \quad j_2 = ie_2 \quad \text{and} \quad j_3 = ie_3.$$

To discuss the real forms of the complex Lie algebra A_1, we use still another basis, which corresponds to the root space decomposition of this algebra. The Cartan subalgebras of the complex simple Lie algebra A_1 are one-dimensional. The selection of a Cartan subalgebra is described in angular momentum theory as choosing a quantization axis. It is conventional to choose $h = j_3 = ie_3$ as the basis of a Cartan subalgebra, but of course one could equally well have chosen j_1 or j_2 for instance. Note however that there are one-dimensional subalgebras, such as the one spanned by the vector $j_1 + ij_2$, which are not Cartan subalgebras. With the chosen vector h as a basis for the Cartan subalgebra H, the dual basis for H^* is given by the linear form α on H satisfying

$$\alpha(h) = 1.$$

The roots of the Lie algebra A_1 with respect to H are the three linear forms 0, $+\alpha$ and $-\alpha$. The corresponding root vectors are

$$e_\alpha = j_+ = j_1 + ij_2 \quad \text{and} \quad e_{-\alpha} = j_- = j_1 - ij_2,$$

which together with h form a basis for the three-dimensional complex Lie algebra A_1. We have

$$[h, e_\alpha] = e_\alpha, \quad [h, e_{-\alpha}] = -e_{-\alpha}, \quad [e_\alpha, e_{-\alpha}] = 2h.$$

The compact real form of A_1 is the original real Lie algebra $su(2) \approx so(3, \mathbb{R})$, since the corresponding Lie groups $SU(2)$ and $SO(3, \mathbb{R})$ are both compact. The compact real form can also be obtained from the general prescription given earlier. According to this prescription, we should have

$$ih = -e_3, \quad i(e_\alpha + e_{-\alpha}) = -2e_1 \quad \text{and} \quad e_\alpha - e_{-\alpha} = -2e_2$$

as a basis for $su(2)$, which it obviously is.

To obtain the other real forms of A_1, we study the involutive auto-morphisms of the compact real form. Since an involutive automorphism S_0 of $su(2)$ satisfies $S_0^2 = 1$, it can only have ± 1 as eigenvalues. If all its eigenvalues were $+1$, then S_0 would be the identity, and the real form generated by it would just be $su(2)$ again. The condition that S_0 be a Lie algebra automorphism is

$$S_0([x, y]) = [S_0(x), S_0(y)]$$

for all x and y in the Lie algebra. If all the eigenvalues of S_0 were -1, then $S_0 = -1$, and

$$[S_0(e_1), S_0(e_2)] = [-e_1, -e_2] = +e_3,$$

while

$$S_0([e_1, e_2]) = S_0(e_3) = -e_3,$$

so that S_0 could not be an automorphism. Thus, any nontrivial involutive automorphism must have at least one eigenvalue $+1$ and one eigenvalue -1, and the eigenspaces L_0^+ and L_0^- are both nonzero. Letting x and y, be corresponding eigenvectors, we have

$$S_0([x, y]) = [S_0(x), S_0(y)] = [x, -y] = -[x, y]$$

so that $[x, y]$ is also an eigenvector corresponding to the eigenvalue -1, that is,

$$[L_0^+, L_0^-] \subset L_0^-.$$

Similarly the products

$$[L_0^-, L_0^-] \subset L_0^+$$

and

$$[L_0^+, L_0^+] \subset L_0^+$$

follow from the fact that S_0 is an automorphism. Since $[x, y]$ is the vector cross product of x and y, it is a nonzero vector orthogonal to both x and y, and hence L_0^- must be two-dimensional, containing the two linearly independent vectors y and $[x, y]$, while L_0^+ is one-dimensional. The vectors y and $[x, y]$ are an orthogonal basis for the eigenspace L_0^-, and since $[L_0^-, L_0^-] \subset L_0^+$, we see that

$$[y, [x, y]] \in L_0^+ .$$

But this implies that $[y, [x, y]]$ is a multiple of x because L_0^+ is one-dimensional, and hence x is orthogonal also to y. Thus x, y and $[x, y]$ are mutually orthogonal vectors, and if x and y are taken to be unit vectors, then $[x, y]$ will also be a unit vector. We can assume that $e_1 = x$, $e_2 = y$ and $e_3 = [x, y]$ without loss of generality. There is thus, up to isomorphism, only one noncompact real form of A_1, corresponding to the automorphism

$$S_0 = \begin{bmatrix} 1 & 0 & 0 \\ 0 & -1 & 0 \\ 0 & 0 & -1 \end{bmatrix}$$

of the compact real form $L_0 = su(2)$. Since L_0^+ is spanned by e_1, and L_0^- is spanned by e_2 and e_3, a basis for the noncompact real form $L_1 = L_0^+ \oplus iL_0^-$ is given by the vectors e_1, ie_2 and ie_3. The Lie products of these basis elements are of course given by

$$[e_1, ie_2] = ie_3, \quad [ie_2, ie_3] = -e_1, \quad [ie_3, e_1] = ie_2.$$

The real Lie algebra so obtained is the real Lie algebra of several Lie groups, including the plane Lorentz group $SO(2, 1; \mathbb{R})$ leaving invariant the form

$$x^2 + y^2 - t^2,$$

the real special linear group $SL(2, \mathbb{R})$, the real symplectic group $Sp(1, \mathbb{R})$ and the pseudo-unitary group $SU(1, 1)$. All of these Lie groups are, of course, locally isomorphic since their Lie algebras are isomorphic. The representations of these noncompact groups have been studied extensively [17], [32], [193].

The real Lie algebras related to the complex Lie algebra A_1 include not only the two real forms discussed above, but also the real restriction A_1^R of A_1.

The real restriction A_1^R is a six-dimensional real Lie algebra, a basis being given by

$$e_1, e_2, e_3, \quad j_1 = ie_1, \quad j_2 = ie_2 \quad \text{and} \quad j_3 = ie_3.$$

The real Lie algebra A_1^R is the Lie algebra of several familiar Lie groups, which are again locally isomorphic. These include the ordinary homogeneous Lorentz group $SO(3, 1; \mathbb{R})$ leaving invariant the form

$$x^2 + y^2 + z^2 - t^2,$$

the complex special linear group $SL(2, \mathbb{C})$ and the complex orthogonal group $SO(3, \mathbb{C})$.

2.18 ANGULAR MOMENTUM THEORY

It may be of interest to further elaborate on the use of complexification and real forms in angular momentum theory. The theory of the rotation group is, after all, one of the main applications of Lie algebraic ideas to quantum mechanics. This theory, also known as the *quantum theory of angular momentum*, is extensively used in atomic and nuclear physics.

The complex Hilbert space of all quantum mechanical state vectors may be regarded as a module over the complex Lie algebra A_1 of the three-dimensional rotation group. Thus the elements of A_1 act as linear operators on this Hilbert space. An explicit realization of these operators can be obtained by quantizing the classical theory. The quantum mechanical operator corresponding to the classical orbital angular momentum

$$\mathbf{l} = \mathbf{r} \times \mathbf{p}$$

for a single particle is obtained by replacing the momentum $\mathbf{p}$ by the differential operator $-i\hbar\nabla$, obtaining

$$\mathbf{L} = -i\hbar\mathbf{r} \times \nabla.$$

The operators $\mathbf{L}$ are Hermitian, and they satisfy the commutation relations

$$L_m L_n - L_n L_m = i\varepsilon_{mnp} L_p,$$

where we have set $\hbar = 1$ for convenience. Adding also the spin $\mathbf{S}$, for which there is no completely satisfactory classical analogue, we obtain the total angular momentum

$$\mathbf{J} = \mathbf{L} + \mathbf{S}$$

for a single particle. One now postulates that the operators $\mathbf{J}$ are also Hermitian, and satisfy the same commutation relations as $\mathbf{L}$, namely,

$$J_m J_n - J_n J_m = i\varepsilon_{mnp} J_p.$$

The formal theory of angular momentum is built up on the basis of these commutation relations and Hermiticity requirements alone [84], [203]. One of the main roles of the Hermiticity assumption in angular momentum theory is just to argue that the unitary representations of the rotation group must be finite-dimensional. If we drop this Hermiticity requirement, then the resulting theory can also be applied to the finite-dimensional nonunitary representations of the Lorentz group. To discuss the representation theory of A_1 one customarily defines operators

$$J_\pm = J_1 \pm iJ_2$$

so that the commutation relations become

$$[J_3, J_+] = J_+, \quad [J_3, J_-] = -J_- \quad \text{and} \quad [J_+, J_-] = 2J_3.$$

If ψ is an eigenvector in Hilbert space such that $J_3\psi = m\psi$, then $J_\pm\psi$ are either zero or else eigenvectors of J_3 with eigenvalues $m \pm 1$. This shows that J_+ raises the eigenvalue by one unit and J_- lowers the eigenvalue by one unit; hence we have the terms "raising" and "lowering operators."

The theory of the Lorentz group is the relativistic generalization of angular momentum theory. To develop this theory one may proceed heuristically, starting with the classical description of a relativistic spinning particle. The equation

$$\mathbf{J} = \mathbf{X} \times \mathbf{P} + \mathbf{S}$$

generalizes to the formula

$$M^{\mu\nu} = X^\mu P^\nu - X^\nu P^\mu + S^{\mu\nu}$$

for the generators of the homogeneous Lorentz group, where $\mu, \nu = 0, 1, 2, 3$. Here $X^0 = t$ is the time and $P^0 = E$ is the total energy, and we have set the velocity of light equal to unity, $c \doteq 1$. The energy and momentum of course must be given by their relativistic expressions. The momentum of a free particle with rest mass m and velocity v is given by

$$\mathbf{P} = m\mathbf{v}/\sqrt{1 - v^2},$$

while the energy is given by

$$E = m/\sqrt{1 - v^2}.$$

Since $M^{\mu\nu}$ is antisymmetric, it has six independent nonzero components, including the three components of angular momentum

$$J_1 = M^{23}, \quad J_2 = M^{31} \quad \text{and} \quad J_3 = M^{12}$$

and three components called *Lorentz boosts*,

$$K_1 = M^{10}, \quad K_2 = M^{20} \quad \text{and} \quad K_3 = M^{30}.$$

The components of $\mathbf{J}$ generate ordinary rotations, while those of $\mathbf{K}$ generate pure Lorentz transformations, that is, Lorentz transformations which preserve a space-like plane.

For the corresponding quantum mechanical theory, these classical quantities must all be replaced by Hermitian operators defined on a common dense domain of Hilbert space and satisfying appropriate commutation relations. One is naturally led to postulate the commutation relations

$$X^\mu P^\nu - P^\nu X^\mu = ig^{\mu\nu}1,$$

where the metric tensor $g^{\mu\nu}$ is $+1$ if $\mu = \nu = 1, 2$ or 3, and $g^{00} = -1$, while all the other components vanish. Since these commutation relations imply that the position operators X^μ fail to commute with the mass operator $P^\mu P_\mu$, they are seldom used in practice for the description of particles having a definite mass [13]. Instead, the kinematics of relativistic particles with spin is completely described in terms of the generators $M^{\mu\nu}$ of the Lorentz group and the momenta P^ν. Together, the six generators $M^{\mu\nu}$ of the Lorentz group and the four components P^ν of momentum span the ten-dimensional Lie algebra of the Poincaré group. Practical applications of the Poincaré group in elementary particle physics deal with the helicity representation for partial-wave expansions of high-energy scattering amplitudes [132], [172].

The *Poincaré group*, or inhomogeneous Lorentz group, is the group of transformations of the four-dimensional Minkowski space-time which preserve distances between points. The Poincaré group is not semisimple since the set of all parallel translations of space-time forms an Abelian normal subgroup. The homogeneous *Lorentz group* is defined to be the quotient group of the Poincaré group modulo its translation subgroup. The Lorentz group may alternatively be described as the set of all elements of the Poincaré group which leave fixed an arbitrary specified point of space-time. The whole Poincaré group is then generated by the translation subgroup and any one of these Lorentz subgroups. The corresponding breakup of the Poincaré Lie algebra as a direct sum of the Abelian ideal generating translations and a simple subalgebra generating Lorentz transformations is a Levi decomposition for this algebra.

To clarify the structure of the Poincaré and Lorentz Lie algebras further, we examine the commutation relations for $M^{\mu\nu}$ and P^ν. The relations

$$P^\mu P^\nu - P^\nu P^\mu = 0$$

show that the translation subalgebra is Abelian, while

$$M^{\mu\nu}P^\lambda - P^\lambda M^{\mu\nu} = i(g^{\mu\lambda}P^\nu - g^{\nu\lambda}P^\mu)$$

shows that it is an ideal. The generators of the Lorentz subgroup satisfy the commutation relations

$$M^{\mu\nu}M^{\rho\sigma} - M^{\rho\sigma}M^{\mu\nu} = i\{g^{\mu\rho}M^{\nu\sigma} + g^{\nu\sigma}M^{\mu\rho} - g^{\nu\rho}M^{\mu\sigma} - g^{\mu\sigma}M^{\nu\rho}\}.$$

Although the real Lie algebra A_1^R of the Lorentz group is simple, its complexification is not simple, but only semisimple, splitting up as $A_1 \dotplus A_1$. We may note, by the way, that $SO(4, \mathbb{R})$ and $SO(3, \mathbb{R}) \times SO(3, \mathbb{R})$ have real Lie algebras isomorphic to $su(2) \dotplus su(2)$, whose complexification also yields $A_1 \dotplus A_1$. In other words, both A_1^R and $su(2) \dotplus su(2)$ are real forms of the same semisimple complex Lie algebra $A_1 \dotplus A_1$.

As a consequence, the theory of the Lie algebra of the Lorentz group may be described as a doubled version of angular momentum theory. In fact, the commutation relations of the Lorentz algebra, which may of course be rewritten in terms of **J** and **K**, acquire a simple form if we set

$$\mathbf{J}^{\pm} = \tfrac{1}{2}(\mathbf{J} \pm i\mathbf{K}).$$

What emerges then is the explicit $A_1 \dotplus A_1$ structure of the complexified Lie algebra of the Lorentz group,

$$[J_k^{\pm}, J_l^{\pm}] = i\varepsilon_{klm}J_m^{\pm}, \qquad [J_k^{+}, J_l^{-}] = 0.$$

Although **J** and **K** are Hermitian operators, the operators $\mathbf{J}^{\pm}$ are not, and because of this, the Lorentz group can have infinite-dimensional unitary irreducible representations [182].

CHAPTER 3

CONSTRUCTIVE METHODS

3.1 RAISING AND LOWERING SUBALGEBRAS

Any module over a Lie algebra may also be regarded as a module over its universal enveloping associative algebra. We may therefore use the representation theory of associative algebras to clarify the structure of Lie modules. For example, the universal enveloping algebra plays an important part in constructing the irreducible modules over a semisimple Lie algebra. For this purpose we need to take a quick look at the structure of the enveloping algebra of a semisimple Lie algebra L resulting from its root space decomposition. We choose a Cartan subalgebra H and denote the subspaces of L spanned respectively by the root vectors of the positive and negative roots by L^+ and L^-. The subspaces L^+ and L^- are nilpotent subalgebras of L generated respectively by the simple raising and lowering elements, and we can write

$$L = H \oplus L^+ \oplus L^-.$$

Corresponding to this breakup of the Lie algebra L into H, L^+ and L^-, we can also break up the universal enveloping algebra $U(L)$ into three parts U^0, U^+ and U^-. Here U^0 is the Abelian subalgebra generated by the identity element and the Cartan subalgebra H, while U^+ and U^- are generated by the identity element together with L^+ and L^-, respectively. We may call U^+ and U^- respectively the *raising algebra* and *lowering algebra* of the Lie algebra L. The whole enveloping algebra $U(L)$ may be written as the product of the three subalgebras U^0, U^+ and U^-, taken in any order. The algebra U^+ is generated by the identity and the simple raising elements, while U^- is generated by the identity and the simple lowering elements. Since the Cartan subalgebra H is spanned by the commutators of simple raising and lowering elements, the whole universal enveloping algebra $U(L)$ is generated by the identity and the simple raising and lowering elements.

The lowering algebra U^- is a useful tool for obtaining the direct sum decomposition of a reducible module M over a semisimple Lie algebra L. An *extreme vector* x in a module M is a nonzero vector which is annihilated by all the simple raising elements $e_1, \cdots, e_l$ in the sense that

$$e_i x = 0$$

91

for $i = 1, \cdots, l$. Since the root vector e_α of any positive root α is generated by the simple raising elements $e_1, \cdots, e_l$, any extreme vector x also satisfies the more general condition

$$e_\alpha x = 0$$

for $\alpha > 0$. The extreme vectors together with the zero vector form a subspace, the *extreme subspace* of the module. If a module is irreducible, its extreme subspace is one-dimensional, and is spanned by a weight vector v for the highest weight λ. Indeed, for any $\alpha > 0$, the vector $e_\alpha v$ would be a weight vector for the higher weight $\lambda + \alpha$ if it were not zero. In any module M, the subspace $U^- x$ is an irreducible submodule if x is an extreme vector. Moreover, any basis $x_1, \cdots, x_n$ of its extreme subspace yields a decomposition of the module M as a direct sum of irreducible submodules

$$M = U^- x_1 \oplus \cdots \oplus U^- x_n.$$

Thus a knowledge of the extreme subspace yields a reduction of the module to a direct sum of irreducible submodules, which is a valuable technique, for instance, in computing Clebsch–Gordan coefficients.

Irreducible modules can be generated not only by their extreme vectors, but by any nonzero element. To do this, however, we have to use the whole enveloping algebra, not just the lowering subalgebra. Thus if x is any element of an irreducible module M over a Lie algebra L, then we have $M = U(L)x$. That is, every vector $y \in M$ can be written as $y = ux$ for some element $u \in U(L)$. By use of this result it becomes possible to construct the irreducible modules themselves out of the enveloping algebra $U(L)$. To do this, we need not assume that the Lie algebra L is semisimple, and we may treat a class of modules slightly more general than the irreducible ones.

A module M over a Lie algebra L is called a *cyclic module* if there is a vector x in M such that

$$M = U(L)x.$$

If we regard $U(L)$ as a module over itself, the mapping which takes any element $u \in U(L)$ into the vector $ux \in M$ may be described as a module homomorphism from $U(L)$ onto M. The kernel of this module homomorphism is a submodule, and hence a left ideal, of $U(L)$ which we call the *annihilator* of the cyclic module M. The annihilator A does not depend on x, and may be described as the set of elements $a \in U(L)$ such that $av = 0$ for all $v \in M$. By the fundamental homomorphism theorem, the module M is isomorphic to $U(L)/A$, the element ux in M corresponding to the coset $u + A$ in $U(L)/A$. This result, $M \approx U(L)/A$, means that every cyclic module may be obtained as a quotient of $U(L)$ with respect to some left ideal. The problem of finding all the irreducible representations of $U(L)$, and consequently of L, is equivalent to that of finding all the maximal left ideals of $U(L)$. Conversely, if A is a left ideal of $U(L)$, then the cosets form a cyclic module $U(L)/A$ over L, and this module is irreducible if and only if A is a maximal left ideal.

3.2 DYNKIN INDICES

The problem of classifying the irreducible modules over a semisimple Lie algebra has been reduced to finding all possible highest weights. We may use the lowering algebra to show that the set of vectors in H_R^* which can be highest weights for irreducible modules is closed under addition. To see this, let M_1 and M_2 be irreducible modules with extreme vectors x_1 and x_2 corresponding to the highest weights λ_1 and λ_2, respectively. Then $x_1 \otimes x_2$ is an extreme vector in the tensor product module $M_1 \otimes M_2$, and applying the lowering algebra, we obtain the irreducible submodule $U^-(x_1 \otimes x_2)$ having $\lambda_1 + \lambda_2$ as its highest weight. The submodule $U^-(x_1 \otimes x_2)$, sometimes denoted by $\overline{M_1 \otimes M_2}$, is called the *Cartan composition* of the modules M_1 and M_2. The Cartan composition of two irreducible modules is that irreducible submodule of their tensor product which corresponds to the highest weight. A *basic weight* is a highest weight which is not the sum of two nonzero highest weights. The number of basic weights of a semisimple Lie algebra is equal to its rank l. An irreducible module is said to be a *basic module* if its highest weight is one of the basic weights.

The basic weights satisfy a number of interesting relations which make them useful as a basis for the space H_R^*. We can number the basic weights $\lambda_1, \cdots, \lambda_l$ to correspond to the simple roots $\alpha_1, \cdots, \alpha_l$ so that

$$2(\lambda_i, \alpha_j)/(\alpha_j, \alpha_j)$$

is zero if $i \neq j$ and one if $i = j$. From these formulas and a knowledge of the simple roots, one can construct the basic weights either geometrically or algebraically. Any weight μ is a linear combination of basic weights,

$$\mu = m_1\lambda_1 + \cdots + m_l\lambda_l,$$

with integer coefficients

$$m_i = 2(\lambda, \alpha_i)/(\alpha_i, \alpha_i)$$

called the *Dynkin indices* of the weight μ. The Dynkin indices of the highest weight uniquely characterize an irreducible module over a semisimple Lie algebra up to isomorphism. In general the Dynkin indices of a weight can be any integers, positive, zero or negative, but the Dynkin indices of a highest weight are always nonnegative. The Dynkin indices of the simple roots α_j are given by the elements of the Cartan matrix $[A_{ij}]$, where

$$A_{ij} = 2(\alpha_i, \alpha_j)/(\alpha_i, \alpha_i),$$

and we may thus write

$$\alpha_j = \sum_{i=1}^{l} \lambda_i A_{ij}.$$

The action of the Weyl group on the weight system of a module is particularly easy to compute in terms of Dynkin indices. Each basic weight is invariant under all but one of the simple Weyl reflections since $w_i \lambda_j = \lambda_j$ for $i \neq j$, while $w_i \lambda_i = \lambda_i - \alpha_i$. Hence the Dynkin indices m'_i of the reflected weight $w_j \mu$ are related to the indices m_i of μ itself by the relation

$$m'_i = m_i - A_{ij} m_j.$$

We may construct an irreducible module with highest weight

$$\lambda = \sum_i n_i \lambda_i$$

in terms of a set of basic modules $M_1, \cdots, M_l$. This module is the Cartan composition

$$U^-(x_1 \otimes \cdots \otimes x_1 \otimes \cdots \otimes x_l \otimes \cdots \otimes x_l),$$

where the weight vector x_i in M_i, for the basic highest weight λ_i, appears n_i times in the tensor product. Thus the process of Cartan composition reduces the problem of constructing the irreducible modules of a semisimple Lie algebra to that of constructing its basic modules.

Dynkin introduced a convenient way of specifying the irreducible modules over a semisimple Lie algebra [83]. One simply writes the ith Dynkin index of the highest weight above the ith vertex of the Dynkin diagram of the Lie algebra. In Fig. 5 this is illustrated for a particular representation of the Lie algebra B_3, the complexification of the real Lie algebra of $SO(7, \mathbb{R})$.

1   0   0

FIG. 5. *Dynkin diagram for the 8-dimensional spinor module of B_3, which can be used to define the exceptional Lie algebra G_2*

This particular module is the 8-dimensional spinor module of B_3, which is of special interest because it can be used to define the exceptional simple Lie algebra G_2. One may in fact obtain G_2 as the subalgebra of all elements in B_3 which annihilate a certain vector of this module [27].

Besides the Dynkin diagram notation, we shall also use the common notation {N} to denote an irreducible module of dimension N. The main advantage of this notation is that it is concise, while the Dynkin diagram notation has the advantage of supplying more pertinent information which is useful for computations. In some cases, there are several nonisomorphic irreducible modules with the same dimension, which may be distinguished by adding primes, asterisks, and so forth. For example, the dual of the module {N} is denoted by {N*}. For Lie algebras of type B_l or C_l and for Lie algebras of type D_l with even l, as well as for the particular algebras A_1, G_2, F_4, E_7

and E_8, each module is isomorphic to its own dual [161]. The dual operation thus plays no particularly important role for these Lie algebras, while for the remaining algebras, many but not all modules are self-dual. In practice, the main application of duality in the representation theory of simple Lie algebras is to Lie algebras of type A_l with $l \geq 2$. For an irreducible module over A_l, the Dynkin indices of the dual module may be obtained by replacing m_i by m_{l+1-i}.

3.3   IRREDUCIBLE REPRESENTATIONS OF A_1

We now discuss an important example, the computation of the irreducible representations of the complexified Lie algebra A_1 of the ordinary rotation group $SO(3, \mathbb{R})$. Any representation of $SO(3, \mathbb{R})$ is a homomorphism into the group of nonsingular linear operators on a vector space, and its kernel is a closed normal subgroup. The kernel must be all of $SO(3, \mathbb{R})$ or just the identity, and such a representation either trivially maps all of $SO(3, \mathbb{R})$ onto the identity, or it is a one-to-one mapping. The composition of any representation of $SO(3, \mathbb{R})$ with the canonical projection of its covering group $SU(2)$ onto $SO(3, \mathbb{R})$ yields a representation of the group $SU(2)$. Moreover, the image of any normal subgroup of $SU(2)$ under the canonical projection is a normal subgroup of $SO(3, \mathbb{R})$, and hence the only proper closed normal subgroup of $SU(2)$ consists of $\pm I$. The representations of $SU(2)$ which can be obtained from those of $SO(3, \mathbb{R})$ are those which are not faithful, having kernels which contain the negative of the identity, $-I$.

When we pass to the simple complex Lie algebra A_1, we obtain all the representations of $SU(2)$, not just those which arise from the representations of the rotation group. Instead of the usual basis j_1, j_2, j_3 for the Lie algebra A_1, we again use the basis consisting of $h = j_3$ and $e_{\pm\alpha} = j_{\pm} = j_1 \pm ij_2$, which satisfies

$$[h, e_{\pm\alpha}] = \pm e_{\pm\alpha} \quad \text{and} \quad [e_\alpha, e_{-\alpha}] = 2h.$$

There is a Cartan subalgebra H with basis h, and roots $0, \pm\alpha$, where $\alpha(h) = 1$. Since the sum of the squares of the lengths of the roots equals the rank, which is one, we have $(\alpha, \alpha) = \frac{1}{2}$. The raising and lowering algebras U^+ and U^- consist, respectively, of all polynomials in e_α and in $e_{-\alpha}$. There is one basic weight λ in the one-dimensional space $H_{\mathbb{R}}^*$, and since it is a multiple of α satisfying

$$2(\lambda, \alpha)/(\alpha, \alpha) = 1,$$

it must be $\lambda = \alpha/2$.

In the quantum theory of angular momentum, the basic module over A_1 is known as the *spinor representation*, or the *spin-half representation* of the rotation group [190]. The weight vector x corresponding to the highest weight λ satisfies

$$hx = \tfrac{1}{2}x$$

and is an extreme vector, so that

$$e_\alpha x = 0.$$

Since the basic weight λ goes over into its negative under a Weyl reflection, the weight system of the basic module consists at least of $\pm\lambda$, and in fact consists of these two weights alone. Since

$$e_\alpha e_{-\alpha}x = [e_\alpha, e_{-\alpha}]x + e_{-\alpha}e_\alpha x = x,$$

it follows that $y = e_{-\alpha}x$ is nonzero and hence is a weight vector for the shifted weight $\lambda - \alpha = -\lambda$. We must have $e_{-\alpha}y = 0$, because if it were nonzero, we would obtain a weight lower than $-\lambda$, and by Weyl reflection one higher than λ. Hence the spinor space $U^- x$ is a two-dimensional complex vector space spanned by the two basis vectors x and y. The action of A_1 on the basic module is given by

$$hx = \tfrac{1}{2}x, \qquad hy = -\tfrac{1}{2}y,$$

$$e_\alpha x = e_{-\alpha}y = 0,$$

$$e_{-\alpha}x = y, \qquad e_\alpha y = x.$$

Rewriting this action in terms of the basis j_1, j_2, j_3 yields the *Pauli matrices*,

$$\sigma_1 = \begin{bmatrix} 0 & 1 \\ 1 & 0 \end{bmatrix}, \quad \sigma_2 = \begin{bmatrix} 0 & -i \\ i & 0 \end{bmatrix} \quad \text{and} \quad \sigma_3 = \begin{bmatrix} 1 & 0 \\ 0 & -1 \end{bmatrix}.$$

The linear mapping which takes j_k into $\tfrac{1}{2}\sigma_k$ for $k = 1, 2, 3$ is precisely what is called the *spin-half representation* of the Lie algebra A_1.

Every irreducible module over A_1 is isomorphic to a module generated by letting the lowering algebra U^- act on a tensor product $x \otimes \cdots \otimes x$. Each irreducible module is therefore characterized by a single integer n, the rank of the tensor $x \otimes \cdots \otimes x$, that is, the number of repetitions of x. The tensor $x \otimes \cdots \otimes x$ is the highest weight of the module, and since

$$h(x \otimes \cdots \otimes x) = (hx) \otimes x \otimes \cdots \otimes x + x \otimes (hx) \otimes \cdots \otimes x$$

$$+ \cdots + x \otimes \cdots \otimes (hx) = (n/2)(x \otimes \cdots \otimes x),$$

the highest weight for the module is $(n/2)\alpha = j\alpha$. In the terminology of angular momentum theory, the number $j = n/2$, which can be either an integer or a half-integer, is called the *spin* of the module [84]. The irreducible modules corresponding to representations of the rotation group are just those having integer spin, while the others are representations only of its covering group. We now calculate the entire module structure, choosing the module basis to agree with the usual conventions of the quantum theory of angular momentum. In the case $n = 2$, corresponding to spin one, we find

$$e_{-\alpha}(x \otimes x) = x \otimes y + y \otimes x,$$

$$e_{-\alpha}(x \otimes y + y \otimes x) = 2y \otimes y.$$

For symmetry, it is convenient to take as basis for this module

$$u_1 = x \otimes x, \quad u_0 = \frac{1}{\sqrt{2}}(x \otimes y + y \otimes x), \quad u_{-1} = y \otimes y.$$

More generally, for the irreducible module M_j with spin j, we can compute a basis of $2j + 1$ vectors u_m, where

$$m = -j, -j + 1, \cdots, +j,$$

with

$$u_j = x \otimes \cdots \otimes x,$$

$$(2j \text{ factors}),$$

$$u_{-j} = y \otimes \cdots \otimes y.$$

This basis can be chosen so that the action of the Lie algebra is given by

$$hu_m = mu_m,$$

$$e_\alpha u_m = \sqrt{(j - m)(j + m + 1)}\, u_{m+1},$$

$$e_{-\alpha} u_m = \sqrt{(j + m)(j - m + 1)}\, u_{m-1}.$$

These formulas are central in the theories of the representations of the ordinary rotation group and of the homogeneous Lorentz group [84], [182].

3.4   THE CASIMIR SUBALGEBRA

The center $C(L)$ of the universal enveloping algebra $U(L)$ is a key element in the computational aspects of representation theory [147], [229]. It is an Abelian subalgebra consisting of those elements z in $U(L)$ which commute with every element of the Lie algebra L. For a semisimple Lie algebra L, there is always one such element which can be constructed as follows. Let $e_1, \cdots, e_n$ be any basis for the Lie algebra L; since L is semisimple, its Killing form is nonsingular, and there exists another basis $e^1, \cdots, e^n$ for L such that

$$(e^i, e_j) = \delta^i_j.$$

The element

$$\gamma = \sum_{i=1}^{n} e^i e_i$$

of the universal enveloping algebra, called the *second order Casimir element* of L, commutes with every element of the Lie algebra [49]. The second order Casimir element for a semisimple Lie algebra is analogous to the Laplace operator in the theory of special functions. We can also give a formula for γ which is highly reminiscent of the factorization method for the Laplace operator. If $h_1, \cdots, h_l$ is a basis for a Cartan subalgebra H, then since H is nonsingular, there is another basis $h^1, \cdots, h^l$ such that

$$(h^i, h_j) = \delta_j^i.$$

The second order Casimir element can then be expressed as

$$\gamma = \sum_{i=1}^{l} h^i h_i + \sum_{\alpha \neq 0} \frac{e_\alpha e_{-\alpha}}{(e_\alpha, e_{-\alpha})}.$$

The sum in the second term goes over all the nonzero roots α of L, and e_α is any nonzero root vector in L_H^α.

The second order Casimir element is used in the proof that modules over semisimple Lie algebras are completely reducible [50]. It also has many other uses in the theory of representations of semisimple Lie algebras. In an irreducible module M, the operator corresponding to γ is a multiple of the unit operator, $\gamma = \gamma(M) \cdot 1$. If M has highest weight λ, then the eigenvalue $\gamma(M)$ of the operator representing the second order Casimir invariant in M is given by Weyl's formula

$$\gamma(M) = (\lambda, \lambda + 2\delta),$$

where δ is half the sum of the positive roots. In the adjoint representation of a simple Lie algebra L, we have $\gamma(L) = 1$, and thus the operator corresponding to γ is the unit operator itself. For example, if we take the usual angular momentum basis j_1, j_2, j_3 for the Lie algebra A_1, then the Casimir element γ is

$$\tfrac{1}{2}(j_1^2 + j_2^2 + j_3^2),$$

which has the eigenvalue

$$\tfrac{1}{2}j(j + 1)$$

in an irreducible module with spin j. For the adjoint representation of A_1, the spin is unity, $j = 1$, and $\tfrac{1}{2}j(j + 1) = 1$. The second order Casimir element is a simple example of an element of $C(L)$, and we may think of $C(L)$ as consisting of the Casimir element and its various higher order generalizations. Since the subalgebra $C(L)$ of the universal enveloping algebra contains what are known to physicists as higher order Casimir invariants, it is natural to call $C(L)$ the *Casimir algebra* of L. A *Casimir element* is any element in the center $C(L)$ of the universal enveloping algebra.

For irreducible representations each element of $C(L)$ is represented by a multiple of the identity. Recently, much work has been done to find the relation between the eigenvalues of these higher order Casimir elements and the classification of irreducible modules by their highest weight [5].

For any finite-dimensional module M, we can define a linear form τ on the Casimir algebra by means of the trace,

$$\tau(z) = \mathrm{Tr}_M z,$$

where $z \in C(L)$. The linear form $\tau \in C(L)^*$ characterizes the modules in the sense that if modules M and M' have linear forms τ and τ' which are proportional to each other, then the modules are isomorphic [116].

3.5 IRREDUCIBLE REPRESENTATIONS OF A_2

The simple Lie algebra A_2 is the complexification of the real Lie algebra of the special unitary group $SU(3)$. This particular group has recently been studied extensively in applications dealing with the strongly interacting elementary particles [72]. We recall that the six nonzero roots of A_2 have equal lengths, forming the vertices of a regular hexagon, as shown in Fig. 4 (§ 2.15). Since the sum of the squares of the lengths of all the roots is equal to the rank, which is two, each nonzero root has length $1/\sqrt{3}$. The Killing form can now be computed since the angle between the simple roots α_1 and α_2 is $120°$. We find that

$$(\alpha_1, \alpha_1) = (\alpha_2, \alpha_2) = 1/3$$

and

$$(\alpha_1, \alpha_2) = -1/6.$$

The canonical basis for A_2 consists of the simple raising elements e_1 and e_2, the simple lowering elements f_1 and f_2, their commutators $e_{12} = [e_1, e_2]$ and $f_{12} = [f_1, f_2]$ and the elements h_1 and h_2. The equations defining the basic weights λ_1 and λ_2 can be solved either algebraically or geometrically. These equations say that λ_1 is perpendicular to α_2, and its projection onto α_1 is half the length of α_1, as shown in Fig. 6.

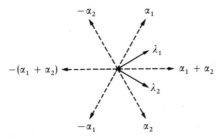

FIG. 6. *Basic weights of the simple Lie algebra A_2 shown superimposed on the root diagram*

Every representation of A_2 can be obtained from the two basic ones. The representation which corresponds to the basic weight λ_2 is just the dual of the one corresponding to λ_1. In the applied literature dealing with the elementary particles, these are known as the *quark* and *antiquark representations.*

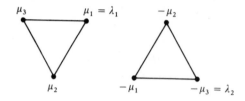

FIG. 7. *Weight diagrams of the two basic modules of A_2*

Using the Weyl group, we find that the weight system of the basic module with highest weight λ_1 is an equilateral triangle consisting of three weights μ_1, μ_2 and μ_3, as shown in Fig. 7. For the basic module M_1 we choose a basis x_1, x_2, x_3 consisting of weight vectors corresponding to the weights μ_1, μ_2, μ_3 respectively, where

$$\mu_1 = \lambda_1, \quad \mu_2 = \lambda_2 - \lambda_1 \quad \text{and} \quad \mu_3 = -\lambda_2.$$

Having chosen the extreme vector x_1, clearly we can define x_2 and x_3 by the equations

$$x_2 = f_1 x_1, \qquad x_3 = f_2 x_2,$$

fixing their relative normalizations.

We can now use the commutation relations of the Lie algebra A_2 to compute the matrices for the representation. As a sample calculation, we note that

$$e_1 x_2 = e_1 f_1 x_1 = [e_1, f_1] x_1 + f_1 e_1 x_1 = h_1 x_1 = x_1,$$

where we used

$$h_i x_j = \mu_j(h_i) x_j$$

and $\lambda_i(h_j) = \delta_{ij}$. The shifting rule $L_H^\alpha M_H^\mu \subset M_H^{\mu+\alpha}$ and an inspection of the weight system shows that

$$e_1 x_1 = e_1 x_3 = 0,$$

so that the only nonzero entry of the matrix corresponding to e_1 is in the first row and second column. A more complete calculation leads to the following matrix representation corresponding to the basic module M_1 over the Lie algebra A_2:

$$e_1 \mapsto \begin{bmatrix} 0 & 1 & 0 \\ 0 & 0 & 0 \\ 0 & 0 & 0 \end{bmatrix}, \quad e_2 \mapsto \begin{bmatrix} 0 & 0 & 0 \\ 0 & 0 & 1 \\ 0 & 0 & 0 \end{bmatrix}, \quad e_{12} \mapsto \begin{bmatrix} 0 & 0 & 1 \\ 0 & 0 & 0 \\ 0 & 0 & 0 \end{bmatrix},$$

$$f_1 \mapsto \begin{bmatrix} 0 & 0 & 0 \\ 1 & 0 & 0 \\ 0 & 0 & 0 \end{bmatrix}, \quad f_2 \mapsto \begin{bmatrix} 0 & 0 & 0 \\ 0 & 0 & 0 \\ 0 & 1 & 0 \end{bmatrix}, \quad f_{12} \mapsto \begin{bmatrix} 0 & 0 & 0 \\ 0 & 0 & 0 \\ -1 & 0 & 0 \end{bmatrix},$$

$$h_1 \mapsto \begin{bmatrix} 1 & 0 & 0 \\ 0 & -1 & 0 \\ 0 & 0 & 0 \end{bmatrix}, \quad h_2 \mapsto \begin{bmatrix} 0 & 0 & 0 \\ 0 & 1 & 0 \\ 0 & 0 & -1 \end{bmatrix}.$$

The weight system of the dual module $M_2 \approx M_1^*$ is obtained from that of M_1 by inversion in the origin. Thus if μ_1, μ_2 and μ_3 are the weights of the basic module M_1, then $-\mu_1$, $-\mu_2$ and $-\mu_3$ are the weights of the basic module M_2. If we use the dual basis x_1^*, x_2^*, x_3^* in the dual module M_1^*, then the representation matrices in the dual module are the negative transposes of those computed above.

The representation matrices in an arbitrary irreducible representation of A_2 can be obtained by a calculation similar to the one performed above. By using the second and third order Casimir elements of A_2, one can also derive general formulas for these matrices [14].

3.6 CHARACTERS

The *character* of a finite-dimensional module M over a group G is a complex-valued function $\chi : G \to \mathbb{C}$ defined for all g in G by

$$\chi(g) = \mathrm{Tr}_M g.$$

Here $\mathrm{Tr}_M g$ denotes the trace of g, where we regard g as a linear operator on the vector space M. Isomorphic modules have the same character because the trace is invariant under a similarity transformation.

To make the transition from group theory to Lie algebra theory in the discussion of characters, we proceed as follows. Let G be a compact and connected Lie group corresponding to a semisimple complex Lie algebra, obtained for example by exponentiation. The subgroup corresponding to a Cartan subalgebra is a maximal *torus subgroup*, that is, a compact Abelian subgroup isomorphic to the direct product of a number of circle groups. Every element of the group G is conjugate to some element of this maximal torus subgroup [73], [92]. We recall that elements g_1 and g_2 are *conjugate* if there is an element s in the group such that $g_2 = sg_1s^{-1}$. Since the character takes on the same value at conjugate elements of the group, it is determined by its restriction to such a maximal torus subgroup.

This leads us to define the character of a finite-dimensional module over a semisimple complex Lie algebra as a complex-valued function on a Cartan subalgebra. The *character* χ of a module M over a Lie algebra L with Cartan subalgebra H is defined by

$$\chi(h) = \mathrm{Tr}_M \exp h$$

for all h in H. In this definition of the character we regard h as a linear operator acting on the finite-dimensional vector space M, and the exponential function is given by its convergent Taylor series.

There are a number of elementary properties of characters. For example, setting $h = 0$, we get the trace of the unit operator in the module M, which is equal to its dimension:

$$\chi(0) = \dim M.$$

Characters are also useful for computing the Clebsch–Gordan series which reduce the tensor products of irreducible modules as direct sums of irreducible submodules. The character of the direct sum $M \dotplus N$ of two modules M and N is the sum of their characters:

$$\chi_{M \dotplus N}(h) = \chi_M(h) + \chi_N(h).$$

This may be proved by choosing a basis in the direct sum which is the union of bases in the summands. The character of the tensor product $M \otimes N$ of two modules is the product of their characters:

$$\chi_{M \otimes N}(h) = \chi_M(h) \cdot \chi_N(h).$$

This may be proved by substituting

$$h^n(x \otimes y) = \sum_{r=0}^{n} \frac{n!}{r!(n-r)!}(h^r x) \otimes (h^{n-r} y)$$

into

$$\exp h = \sum_{n=0}^{\infty} \frac{h^n}{n!}$$

and interchanging the order of summation.

The representation matrices with respect to the dual basis in the dual of a given module over a Lie algebra are obtained from those in the original module by taking the negative transpose. Since the trace is unaffected by the operation of taking transposes, we see that

$$\chi_{M*}(h) = \chi_M(-h).$$

Since any module M is the direct sum of its weight submodules M_H^μ, we can write

$$\chi(h) = \mathrm{Tr}_M \exp h = \sum_\mu \mathrm{Tr}_{M_H^\mu} \exp h.$$

We define the *multiplicity* n_μ of a weight μ to be the dimension of the corresponding weight submodule:

$$n_\mu = \dim M_H^\mu.$$

Consequently the character χ of a module M may be written as

$$\chi(h) = \sum_\mu n_\mu e^{\mu(h)},$$

where the summation goes over all the weights of H in M. This formula shows that a knowledge of the character of a module is equivalent to knowing its weight system and the multiplicity of each weight. Practical methods for computing characters and multiplicities of weights will be discussed later. We may note that the highest weight of an irreducible module over a semisimple Lie algebra has multiplicity one. Also, if w is any element of the Weyl group, then the weights μ and $w\mu$ have the same multiplicity in any module.

3.7 COMPUTATION OF THE KILLING FORM

The first step in performing calculations on the representations of a semisimple Lie algebra on an electronic computing machine is the computation of various quantities related to the Lie algebra itself. This phase includes setting up the Killing metric of the Lie algebra as well as its Cartan matrix and the inverse of the Cartan matrix [83]. The determination of these matrices depends on the choice of simple root labeling. Our choice for the labeling of the simple roots may be seen by inspecting the Dynkin diagrams depicted in Fig. 4 (§ 2.15). Also, the Weyl group and the system of positive roots need to be determined for some of the later calculations. These algorithms can be carried out efficiently using integer-mode arithmetic on a computer [4], [26]. The avoidance of floating-point arithmetic is desirable not only because from theoretical considerations every number is an exact integer, but more importantly because later computations involve tests for equality of numbers which could be seriously affected if roundoff errors were permitted. Roots and weights can be represented as integer arrays by using Dynkin indices, which are their components with respect to a basis consisting of the basic weights $\lambda_1, \cdots, \lambda_l$. In particular, we recall that the entry A_{ij} of the Cartan matrix is the ith component of the jth simple root α_j. The Killing metric is a rational matrix $[g_{ij}]$, where

$$g_{ij} = (\lambda_i, \lambda_j).$$

We can write

$$g_{ij} = G_{ij}/D,$$

where $[G_{ij}]$ is an integer matrix and D is a common denominator. Then we can compute the inner product of any weights $\mu = \sum_i m_i \lambda_i$ and $v = \sum_j n_j \lambda_j$ since

$$(\mu, v) = \sum_{i,j} g_{ij} m_i n_j.$$

A simple way to compute g_{ij} is to start from the quantities

$$(\alpha_i, \alpha_j) = M_{ij}/N$$

which can be read off directly from the Dynkin diagram. Since the Dynkin diagram informs us directly only about relative lengths and angles between simple roots, we only obtain M_{ij} and we will later have to compute the normalization factor N by separate means. We can compute the integer Cartan matrix from

$$A_{ij} = 2M_{ij}/M_{ii},$$

and its inverse may either be obtained directly by a modified Gauss–Jordan reduction procedure or by consulting tables given by Dynkin [83]. Overflow problems can be minimized in the inversion routine by using small nonzero integers as pivot elements and repeatedly reducing fractions to lowest terms, these methods being sufficient up to rank 8. The inverse $[A_{ij}^{-1}]$ is a rational matrix which is represented in the machine as a ratio

$$A_{ij}^{-1} = B_{ij}/d.$$

The formula

$$G_{ij} = B_{ji} M_{jj}$$

(no sum) yields the metric up to the normalization factor D which we can obtain in two different ways. One way, which requires a prior computation of the root system, is to use the fact that the sum of the squares of the lengths of the roots of a semisimple Lie algebra is equal to its rank. For simple Lie algebras, a better procedure is to use the fact that the second order Casimir operator has the value 1 in the adjoint representation. If we know the highest weight of the adjoint representation, that is, the highest root, then this method is computationally much simpler. Indeed, if $r_1, \cdots, r_l$ are the Dynkin indices of the highest root, then

$$D = \sum_{i,j} G_{ij} r_i (r_j + 2)$$

and

$$N = D/(2d).$$

This is just the Weyl formula

$$(\rho, \rho + 2\delta) = 1,$$

where ρ is the highest root and δ is half the sum of the positive roots.

We may illustrate the method for the simple Lie algebra B_2 corresponding to the Lie groups $SO(5, \mathbb{R})$ and $Sp(2)$. From the Dynkin diagram shown in Fig. 8, we obtain

$$M = \begin{bmatrix} 1 & -1 \\ -1 & 2 \end{bmatrix}$$

by inspection, and the Cartan matrix is thus

$$A = \begin{bmatrix} 2 & -2 \\ -1 & 2 \end{bmatrix}.$$

The inverse of the Cartan matrix for B_2 is

$$A^{-1} = \frac{B}{d} = \frac{1}{2}\begin{bmatrix} 2 & 2 \\ 1 & 2 \end{bmatrix},$$

and the metric is given up to normalization by

$$G = \begin{bmatrix} 2 & 2 \\ 2 & 4 \end{bmatrix}.$$

Since the Dynkin indices of the highest root of B_2 are $(2, 0)$, we find $D = 24$ and $N = 6$, and hence the matrix $[g_{ij}]$ is given by

$$\frac{1}{12}\begin{bmatrix} 1 & 1 \\ 1 & 2 \end{bmatrix}.$$

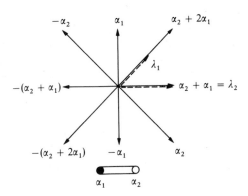

FIG. 8. *Dynkin and Root diagrams of B_2, showing also the basic weights*

3.8 DYNKIN'S ALGORITHM FOR THE WEIGHT SYSTEM

The basic inputs for a given weight diagram calculation are the rank and type of the simple Lie algebra under consideration and the Dynkin indices of the highest weight of the irreducible module whose weight diagram is to be determined. The outputs include the weight system, the multiplicity of each weight, and other pertinent information. Given the highest weight of an irreducible module over a low rank semisimple Lie algebra, finding all the other weights is a simple problem in geometry. Since the Weyl group describes the symmetry properties of weight systems, we need only apply Weyl reflections to the highest weight to obtain the general shape of the weight system. We can then fill in the rest of the weight system by using ladders of weights.

To illustrate this procedure, consider again the simple Lie algebra B_2. The Weyl group of this algebra is generated by the Weyl reflections w_1 and w_2 associated with the simple roots α_1 and α_2. If we introduce Cartesian coordinates (x, y) in the plane of the root system, then w_1 and w_2 are the following maps:

$$w_1: (x, y) \mapsto (x, -y), \quad \text{reflection in the } x\text{-axis},$$

$$w_2: (x, y) \mapsto (y, x), \quad \text{reflection about the line } x = y.$$

Note that

$$w_1^2 = w_2^2 = (w_1 w_2)^4 = 1,$$

where 1 is the identity mapping, since $w_1 w_2$ is a 90° rotation. The Weyl group, consisting of the elements 1, w_1, w_2, $w_1 w_2$, $w_2 w_1$, $w_1 w_2 w_1$, $w_2 w_1 w_2$ and $(w_1 w_2)^2$, is a non-Abelian group of order eight which may be identified as the dihedral group of a square [69]. The two basic modules over B_2 have dimensions four and five, respectively. The weight systems of these basic modules, shown in Fig. 9, are easily obtained by applying Weyl reflections to their highest weights and filling in ladders.

For higher rank semisimple Lie algebras, the geometrical method becomes impractical because we cannot easily draw figures in many dimensions. What we want then is a simple algorithm for finding the weight system from the highest weight which can be used in a program for an electronic computer. Dynkin gave one such algorithm, in which the weight system is

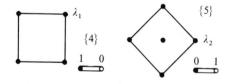

FIG. 9. *Weight diagrams for the basic modules of* B_2

split up into layers, the first layer consisting of the highest weight alone [83], [135]. Each weight in a given layer may be obtained from some parent weight μ contained in the previous layer by subtracting some simple root α_i. To obtain a particular layer, given all the preceding layers, we consider the α_i-ladders passing through all the weights

$$\mu = m_1 \lambda_1 + \cdots + m_l \lambda_l$$

belonging to the previous layer. Since the top and bottom weights of the ladder

$$\mu - p\alpha_i, \cdots, \mu + q\alpha_i$$

are related by the simple Weyl reflection w_i corresponding to the root α_i, we have

$$w_i(\mu + q\alpha_i) = \mu - p\alpha_i.$$

Now $w_i\mu = \mu - m_i\alpha_i$ and $w_i\alpha_i = -\alpha_i$, so that we find

$$p = q + m_i.$$

Since the weights lying above μ in this ladder belong to previous layers, the value of q for this ladder is known and we can compute $p = q + m_i$. The weight $\mu - \alpha_i$ belongs to the given layer if and only if p is positive.

    We illustrate this algorithm in Fig. 10, which summarizes the computation of the weight system for the 16-dimensional irreducible module over B_2 with highest weight (1, 1).

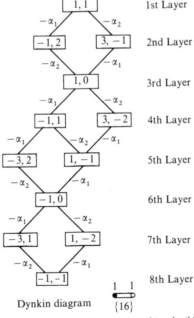

Dynkin diagram   {16}

FIG. 10. *Computation of weights for the 16-dimensional irreducible module for B_2 with highest weight $\lambda = \lambda_1 + \lambda_2$*

From the transpose of the Cartan matrix we can read off the simple roots, which turn out to be $(2, -1)$ and $(-2, 2)$. The weight system, consisting of a total of 12 weights, is shown in Fig. 11.

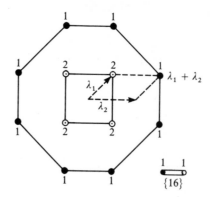

FIG. 11. *Weight diagram (showing multiplicities) for the irreducible module for B_2 with highest weight $\lambda = \lambda_1 + \lambda_2$*

In the process of determining the weight system, it is a good idea to order them lexicographically as well. For this, we do not use the Dynkin indices directly, but first calculate the components of a given weight $\mu = \sum m_i \lambda_i$ with respect to a basis consisting of the simple roots. We do so because lexicographic ordering is defined in terms of the components of a weight with respect to the simple roots rather than in terms of the Dynkin indices, which are their components with respect to the basic weights. We find that

$$\mu = \frac{1}{d} \sum_i p_i \alpha_i,$$

where

$$p_i = \sum_j B_{ij} m_j,$$

and B is the matrix related to the inverse of the Cartan matrix. Then $\mu > 0$, for example, if and only if the first nonzero entry in the new array $(p_1, \cdots, p_l)$ is positive. Thus the process of lexicographic ordering requires a previous computation of the inverse of the Cartan matrix. The final output of the Dynkin layer method is a table of the Dynkin indices of all the weights of a given irreducible module, listed in lexicographic order.

The root system may be computed by the same procedure used to determine the weight systems. To do this, of course, it is necessary to know the highest root of the Lie algebra, which is listed in Fig. 12.

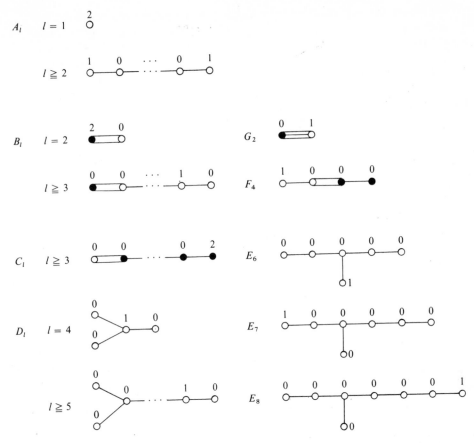

FIG. 12. *Dynkin indices of the highest roots*

For several algorithms to be described later, it is necessary to know all the positive roots. To obtain these, we may apply the Dynkin algorithm to the adjoint representation to obtain the roots, and then lexicographically order the roots to find the positive ones. Another method of calculating the positive roots is to use explicit models of the Lie algebras, in which case we do not need to lexicographically order the roots [81].

3.9 FREUDENTHAL'S ALGORITHM

To compute the character χ_λ of an irreducible module M with highest weight λ over a semisimple Lie algebra L, we need a method for finding the multiplicities of all its weights. There are a number of methods available for computing characters of Lie modules which can be applied uniformly to any type of simple Lie algebra. One of these methods dates back to the early researches of Weyl in 1925–1926 on the representations of semisimple Lie groups [239], [240], [241], [242]. The Weyl method makes use of the Weyl group to generate an object called a girdle, and the character is obtained as a ratio of two girdles. A second method, due to Freudenthal, makes use of a simple algorithm for computing the multiplicities of the weights [89], [90], [91], [92]. This method has the advantage that it avoids the group generated by Weyl reflections, and can therefore handle Lie algebras of large rank. A third method, due to Kostant, also makes use of the Weyl group, but differs from the Weyl method in that the girdle division is replaced by partition function methods [145], [146], [226]. Racah's formula (also developed by Klimyk [140], [196]), involving the Weyl group but no partition function, provides a recursive expression for the multiplicity of the weights. Each of these algorithms presupposes that the weight system has previously been determined. Kostant's method as well as Weyl's original method are sometimes considered to be more elegant than Freudenthal's or Racah's method from a theoretical point of view in that these methods make use of closed formulas rather than recursive procedures.

The real question however is which of these algorithms is most efficient when implemented on a computing machine. To study this question, we have recently experimented with various implementations of these algorithms in FORTRAN and ALGOL. These computations were carried out on the UNIVAC 1108 computer at Carnegie–Mellon University and on the IBM 360/75 system at the University of Pennsylvania [4], [25]. All of these algorithms are practical procedures for computing characters of modules over Lie algebras of rank ≤ 4. The Weyl group rapidly becomes very large with increasing rank, and therefore takes up considerable computing time as well as causing storage problems. If it is only necessary to compute the characters of modules with relatively low dimension, it would seem to be desirable to avoid computing the Weyl group altogether. With the Freudenthal algorithm we were still able to compute characters of modules of dimension up to 1000 for Lie algebras of rank ≤ 8. Thus, this method can be used for all five exceptional simple Lie algebras G_2, F_4, E_6, E_7 and E_8. However, the last three exceptional simple Lie algebras E_6, E_7 and E_8 have comparatively few representations of dimension less than a thousand. On the other hand, for low rank and high dimension the Kostant formula appears to be best, especially if the multiplicities of only certain weights are to be computed.

The Freudenthal algorithm is based on a formula which may be used as a recursion relation to find the multiplicity n_μ of a given weight μ from the multiplicities of higher weights. This recursion relation is

$$\{(\lambda + \delta, \lambda + \delta) - (\mu + \delta, \mu + \delta)\}n_\mu = 2 \sum_{\alpha > 0} \sum_{j=1}^{\infty} n_{\mu + j\alpha}(\mu + j\alpha, \alpha),$$

where $\delta = \sum_{\alpha > 0} \alpha$ denotes half the sum of the positive roots. The sum over α goes over all positive roots, which are known from the root system. The sum over j is not really infinite but breaks off after a finite number of terms.

To use this formula to compute the multiplicities, we start with the multiplicity of the highest weight λ, which we know is unity for an irreducible module. If μ is a weight other than the highest weight, and if we know the multiplicities for all weights $\mu' > \mu$, then each term on the right side of the preceding expression is known. Since for any weight $\mu \neq \lambda$, the quantity

$$(\lambda + \delta, \lambda + \delta) - (\mu + \delta, \mu + \delta)$$

is nonzero and positive, we can always solve for n_μ. The use of the Freudenthal formula can be a lengthy process, but it can be done automatically on a computing machine [4], [26]. Sometimes Freudenthal's algorithm may be made more efficient by making limited use of Weyl reflections and by using the fact that weights related by Weyl reflections have the same multiplicity [148].

As an example of the use of Freudenthal's formula, we consider the simple Lie algebra B_2. We have already computed the metric:

$$(\lambda_1, \lambda_1) = \tfrac{1}{12}, \quad (\lambda_1, \lambda_2) = \tfrac{1}{12}, \quad (\lambda_2, \lambda_2) = \tfrac{1}{6}.$$

The positive roots are α_1, α_2, $\alpha_1 + \alpha_2$ and $2\alpha_1 + \alpha_2$, and half their sum is $\delta = \lambda_1 + \lambda_2$. Now consider again the 16-dimensional module over B_2 with highest weight $\lambda = \lambda_1 + \lambda_2$ which we previously discussed. Its weight system consists of an octagon with a square inside it. Since the eight weights of the octagon are related to the highest weight by the Weyl group, these must have the same multiplicity as the highest weight, that is, one. The four weights of the square inside the octagon are also related to each other by Weyl reflections, and we thus need only compute the multiplicity of one of these. Applying the Freudenthal formula to the case $\mu = \lambda_1$, we calculate

$$(\lambda + \delta, \lambda + \delta) - (\mu + \delta, \mu + \delta) = \tfrac{5}{6}.$$

In the summation over j appearing in the Freudenthal formula only the term with $j = 1$ is nonzero, and we obtain $n_\mu = 2$. Thus the four weights forming the square inside the octagon all have multiplicity two, and the dimension of the module is $8 \times 1 + 4 \times 2 = 16$.

3.10 THE WEYL CHARACTER FORMULA

The Weyl formula for computing characters is conceptionally somewhat simpler than the Freudenthal algorithm. However, Weyl's formula does not turn out to be any easier to implement on an electronic computer. We discuss the Weyl formula mainly because it gives, as a corollary, a useful formula for calculating the dimensions of the irreducible modules, by using the fact that

$$\dim M = \chi(0).$$

The Weyl formula can be proved by purely algebraic means, and has recently also been extended to algebraic groups [48], [218].

For a semisimple Lie algebra, Weyl's formula expresses the character $\chi_\lambda(h)$ of the irreducible module having the highest weight λ as a ratio of two girdles, each girdle also being a linear combination of $e^{\mu(h)}$'s. The coefficients of the $e^{\mu(h)}$'s in a girdle are ± 1, so that the girdles are simpler than the characters themselves. The main computational problems in using the Weyl formula are the generation of the Weyl group needed to compute the girdles and the division of the one girdle by the other. For low rank Lie algebras, the Weyl group is easily obtained, but the girdle division is extremely tedious to carry out by hand. Examples of such calculations for simple Lie algebras of rank two have been given by Behrends, Dreitlein, Fronsdal and Lee [27]. For rank 3, some of these computations are also available in the literature [143], [154].

The coefficients ± 1 occurring in the formula for a girdle are the parities of elements of the Weyl group. The Weyl group W is composed of reflections and products of reflections, each reflection being an orthogonal linear operator with determinant equal to -1. The *parity* det w of an element w in the Weyl group W is equal to $+1$ if w is a product of an even number of reflections and -1 if w is a product of an odd number of reflections. We define the λ-*girdle* as

$$\xi_\lambda(h) = \sum_{w \in W} (\det w) \exp\{[w(\lambda + \delta)](h)\},$$

where δ is half the sum of the positive roots. This quantity δ is also equal to the sum of the basic weights:

$$\delta = \lambda_1 + \cdots + \lambda_l.$$

The Weyl character formula expresses the character of an irreducible module with highest weight λ as the ratio of two girdles:

$$\chi_\lambda(h) = \xi_\lambda(h)/\xi_0(h).$$

The 0-girdle appearing in the denominator is also essential in the derivation of Freudenthal's algorithm.

To clarify the Weyl formula, we introduce some further terminology regarding girdles. The idea here is to work with the algebra of polynomials in the quantities $e^{\mu(h)}$ and allow the Weyl group to operate directly on this algebra. These quantities form a group under multiplication, and the characters and girdles are elements of the group algebra of this group. The *group algebra* of an infinite group G over the complex field is the set of all formal sums $\sum_{g \in G} c_g g$, where the c_g are complex numbers and $c_g = 0$ for all but a finite number of elements $g \in G$. Sums and scalar multiples of elements in the group algebra are defined componentwise, while multiplication is defined by

$$\left(\sum_g c_g g\right)\left(\sum_h d_h h\right) = \sum_g \sum_h (c_g d_h) gh.$$

The group algebra is infinite-dimensional with G as a basis, but no convergence questions arise in these definitions since each element has only a finite number of nonzero components.

The weights μ of any module belong to the set J of all integer linear combinations of the basic weights $\lambda_1, \cdots, \lambda_l$ for a semisimple Lie algebra L. The additive group J is clearly the direct sum of l infinite cyclic groups generated by the basic weights. If e^μ denotes the function which assigns the complex number $e^{\mu(h)}$ to the element $h \in H$, then we may write the character as $\chi = \sum_{\mu \in J} n_\mu e^\mu$. Here we have formally extended the sum so that μ varies over J, this being possible because we have $n_\mu = 0$ when μ is not a weight. The multiplicative group of the quantities e^μ is isomorphic to J since

$$e^\mu e^\nu = e^{\mu + \nu}.$$

The algebra of polynomials in these quantities may thus be identified with the group algebra of J. The identity element of our algebra is e^0, and it is clear that the algebra is both commutative and associative. We turn this group algebra into a module over the Weyl group as follows. For any element w of the Weyl group W, we define the action of w on an element of the group algebra by

$$w\left(\sum_{\mu \in J} c_\mu e^\mu \right) = \sum_{\mu \in J} c_\mu e^{w\mu}.$$

We define an *antisymmetrizer*

$$\mathscr{A} = \sum_{w \in W} (\det w) \cdot w$$

which may be regarded as a linear operator on the group algebra. The definition of the λ-girdle may then be written as

$$\xi_\lambda = \mathscr{A} \, e^{\lambda + \delta},$$

where δ is half the sum of the positive roots, and the Weyl formula may be written as

$$\chi_\lambda = \xi_\lambda / \xi_0.$$

The character χ_λ of a finite-dimensional irreducible Lie module with highest weight λ is sometimes called a *primitive character*. We recall that if two modules are isomorphic, then their characters are equal. To establish the converse, we write

$$\chi_\lambda = e^\lambda + \sum_{\mu < \lambda} n_\mu e^\mu.$$

Since the elements e^λ form a basis for the group algebra, if the characters of two irreducible modules are equal, then their highest weights are equal, and hence the modules are isomorphic. Any finite-dimensional module M over a semisimple Lie algebra is completely reducible. This means that M

can be written in one or more ways as a direct sum of irreducible modules. If m_λ is the number of irreducible modules with highest weight λ in one such decomposition, then the character χ of M is given by

$$\chi = \sum_\lambda m_\lambda \chi_\lambda.$$

Since the primitive characters are linearly independent, the m_λ are uniquely determined, and to this extent at least the reduction of M is unique.

3.11 THE WEYL DIMENSION FORMULA

To obtain the dimension of the irreducible module M_λ from the Weyl character formula, we have to set $h = 0$. The Weyl formula gives the character as a quotient of two girdles

$$\chi_\lambda(h) = \xi_\lambda(h)/\xi_0(h).$$

We cannot simply set $h = 0$ in this expression since $\xi_0(0) = 0$, but we must instead evaluate the limit of this expression as $h \to 0$, using

$$\dim M_\lambda = \chi_\lambda(0) = \lim_{h \to 0} \xi_\lambda(h)/\xi_0(h).$$

Since H_R^* is a Euclidean space, we can regard H as a complexified Euclidean space, and then questions of analysis, such as taking limits, are well-defined.

We can thus use L'Hospital's rule to compute the limit as $h \to 0$ to obtain $\dim M$. First, one can show that the 0-girdle can be written in product form as

$$\xi_0(h) = e^{-\delta(h)} \prod_{\alpha > 0} (e^{\alpha(h)} - 1).$$

We thus see that, for small h,

$$\xi_0(h) \approx \prod_{\alpha > 0} \alpha(h).$$

To obtain the limit as $h \to 0$, we let $h = th_\delta$, where t is a real number and h_δ is an element of H such that

$$(h, h_\delta) = \delta(h).$$

This procedure allows us to relate the λ-girdle to the 0-girdle since one can show that

$$\xi_\lambda(th_\delta) = \xi_0(th_{\lambda + \delta}).$$

Thus we can obtain $\xi_\lambda(th_\delta)$ for small t from the corresponding formula for $\xi_0(th_\delta)$ simply by replacing δ by $\lambda + \delta$, giving

$$\xi_\lambda(th_\delta) \approx \prod_{\alpha > 0} \{t(\alpha, \lambda + \delta)\}.$$

This yields the *Weyl formula* for the dimension of the irreducible module with highest weight λ:

$$\dim M_\lambda = \prod_{\alpha > 0} \frac{(\alpha, \lambda + \delta)}{(\alpha, \delta)}.$$

In using this formula on a computer, there is some danger of overflow for high rank algebras because of the many positive roots. This problem may be minimized by reducing fractions to their lowest terms at frequent intervals in the computation. Better still, one may use to advantage the representation of any nonzero fraction as

$$\pm 2^\alpha 3^\beta 5^\gamma \cdots,$$

where $\alpha, \beta, \gamma, \cdots$ are integers of either sign or zero.

As an example of the Weyl dimension formula, we consider any irreducible module over the simple Lie algebra A_1. The root system for A_1 is $-\alpha, 0, \alpha$ so that there is only one positive root, and thus, half the sum of the positive roots is

$$\delta = \tfrac{1}{2}\alpha.$$

The space H_R^* is one-dimensional and is spanned by the basic weight

$$\lambda_1 = \tfrac{1}{2}\alpha.$$

The highest weight of an irreducible module over A_1 may be written as $\lambda = n\lambda_1$, where n is a nonnegative integer, the Dynkin index of the module. Recall that $j = n/2$ is an integer or half-integer called the spin and $\lambda = n\alpha/2 = j\alpha$. We compute the dimension of any irreducible module with spin j using the Weyl dimension formula. Since there is only one positive root, we have only one factor, and

$$\dim M_\lambda = (\alpha, \lambda + \delta)/(\alpha, \delta) = 2j + 1.$$

For the algebra A_1, it is practical to use the Weyl character formula itself. The Weyl group for the algebra A_1 is

$$W = \{1, w_\alpha\},$$

and the formula for the girdle reduces to two terms. Also, $w_\alpha \mu = -\mu$, and hence,

$$\xi_\lambda = \sum_{w \in W} (\det w) \, e^{w(\lambda + \delta)} = e^{\lambda + \delta} - e^{-(\lambda + \delta)} = e^{(j + 1/2)\alpha} - e^{-(j + 1/2)\alpha}.$$

The character of M_λ is given by the Weyl formula as

$$\chi_\lambda = \frac{\xi_\lambda}{\xi_0} = \frac{e^{(j + 1/2)\alpha} - e^{-(j + 1/2)\alpha}}{e^{\alpha/2} - e^{-\alpha/2}} = \sum_{m = -j}^{+j} e^{m\alpha}.$$

Thus, the weights are

$$-j\alpha, \; -(j-1)\alpha, \; \cdots, \; +j\alpha,$$

each with multiplicity 1.

3.12 CHARACTERS OF MODULES OVER THE ALGEBRA A_2

As a less trivial application of the Weyl character formula, we consider the simple Lie algebra A_2, related to the compact Lie group $SU(3)$. Let Δ be the weight system of the irreducible module over the simple Lie algebra A_2 having highest weight λ, and let

$$\psi_\lambda = \sum_{\mu \in \Delta} e^\mu.$$

Thus ψ_λ is defined almost exactly like the character χ_λ, except that n_μ is replaced by unity for all weights μ belonging to the weight system Δ. Thus ψ_λ can be calculated from a knowledge of the weight system alone, without knowledge of the multiplicities of the weights.

The weight system in general has a hexagonal-type shape, as shown in Fig. 13, and may be obtained from the highest weight $\lambda = p\lambda_1 + q\lambda_2$ by the process of Weyl reflection and filling in ladders.

The girdles of the simple Lie algebra A_2 satisfy the recursion relation

$$\xi_\lambda - \xi_{\lambda-\delta} = \xi_0 \psi_\lambda,$$

from which we may obtain by iteration a formula for the character [7]. For triangular weight systems (those with either p or q equal to zero) we have

$$\chi_\lambda = \psi_\lambda,$$

while for nontriangular weight systems, the recursion relation yields the formula

$$\chi_{\lambda+n\delta} = \psi_\lambda + \psi_{\lambda+\delta} + \cdots + \psi_{\lambda+n\delta}.$$

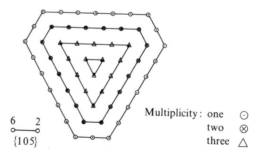

Multiplicity: one   ⊙
                two   ⊗
                three △

$$\begin{matrix} 6 & 2 \\ \circ\!\!-\!\!-\!\!\circ \\ \{105\} \end{matrix}$$

FIG. 13. *Weight diagram of the 105-dimensional representation* $D(6, 2)$ *of* A_2, *showing the multiplicity of each weight*

Here λ is a multiple of either λ_1 or λ_2 and n is a positive integer, while $\delta = \lambda_1 + \lambda_2$ as usual is half the sum of the positive roots. If $p \geqq q$, we may let $\lambda = (p - q)\lambda_1$ and $n = q$, so that $\lambda + n\delta = p\lambda_1 + q\lambda_2$. For $p < q$ we simply interchange the roles of p and q, setting $\lambda = (q - p)\lambda_2$ and $n = p$.

These considerations lead to the following prescriptions for obtaining the character of any irreducible module with highest weight $\lambda = p\lambda_1 + q\lambda_2$ over the algebra A_2. It suffices to consider the case $p \geqq q$, because interchanging p and q is equivalent to taking the dual module. The weight system of the dual module can be obtained by inversion of the weight system of the original module with respect to the origin. This amounts to turning the figure upside down.

For $p \geqq q$ the construction is as follows. First draw a hexagonal-type figure, with sides of alternating lengths of p and q units, each unit being the length of the nonzero roots, which is $1/\sqrt{3}$, so that the horizontal side at the top has length $p/\sqrt{3}$, for example. The interior angle between adjacent sides is 120°. On every side whose length is p (respectively q) units, we then place $p + 1$ (respectively $q + 1$) points spaced at unit intervals, as in Fig. 13. If $q = 0$, the figure degenerates into a triangle. The interior of this figure is now filled with further points arranged in an equilateral triangle-type array, the distance between any two adjacent points being one unit.

This gives us the weight system and it remains to specify their multiplicities. The weight system may be regarded as a series of hexagons of decreasing size, one contained in the other, eventually degenerating into triangles. All weights on the outer perimeter of the figure have multiplicity one. Proceeding inward, each successive hexagon consists of weights whose multiplicity is one more than the previous hexagon, until the multiplicity reaches the value $q + 1$, at which point there is no further increase of multiplicity. In other words, just at the point that the hexagons degenerate into triangles, the multiplicities of the weights stop increasing. Explicit drawings of weight diagrams of modules over A_2 can be found in the literature [72], [106].

3.13 THE KOSTANT AND RACAH CHARACTER FORMULAS

A number of detailed hand computations of characters were published recently in connection with speculations about hadron symmetry schemes in elementary particle physics [183], [217]. We have already mentioned the explicit formula for the multiplicity of any weight of an irreducible module over A_2 which Antoine discovered. Similar, but rather more complicated formulas can be obtained for the other two simple Lie algebras of rank two. The case of the Lie algebra B_2, corresponding to the Lie groups $SO(5, \mathbb{R})$ and $Sp(2)$, has been considered by Gruber and Weber, and by McConnell, while the case of G_2 has been discussed by Radhakrishnan and Santhanam, and by McConnell [111], [165], [166], [199]. For rank three, there are three simple Lie algebras $A_3 \approx D_3$, B_3 and C_3 over the complex numbers. Some early calculations of weight diagrams for the rank three simple Lie algebra A_3, corresponding to the Lie groups $SU(4)$ and $SO(6, \mathbb{R})$, were given in a paper by Wigner over thirty years ago [247]. Some examples of weight diagrams for rank three simple Lie algebras have been given by Loupias, Sirugue and Trotin [154]. The most complete hand calculations for rank three were carried out by Konuma, Shima and Wada [143]. For higher rank algebras, fewer results have been reported in the literature. Examples of weight multiplicity tables for the exceptional simple Lie algebra F_4 are given by Dynkin and Veldkamp [83], [231]. Speiser has given the weight diagrams for the basic modules of Lie algebras of the types A_l, B_l and D_l (see [216]). Several other multiplicity tables have also appeared in the literature [90], [218]. The difficulty of the hand computations led to considerable discussion of improvements in computational methods [109], [110].

Kostant gave another character formula which is closely related to the Weyl character formula. The Kostant formula provides a closed form expression for the multiplicity n_μ for any weight μ of the irreducible module with highest weight λ over a semisimple Lie algebra [145], [146]. In a sense, the Kostant formula is obtained from the Weyl character formula by formally carrying out the girdle division. To do this, one uses a *partition function* $P(\mu)$ defined for all linear forms μ in H_R^* as the number of ways of writing μ as a linear combination of positive roots with nonnegative integers as coefficients. That is, $P(\mu)$ is the number of ways of writing

$$\mu = \sum_{\alpha > 0} k_\alpha \alpha,$$

where $k_\alpha \geqq 0$ is an integer and α a positive root. Kostant's formula is

$$n_\mu = \sum_{w \in W} (\det w) P[w(\lambda + \delta) - (\mu + \delta)].$$

It was suggested by Antoine and Speiser that the Kostant formula might save computation time, particularly for high rank Lie algebras and for high-dimensional representations [8], [9]. The computation of the partition function is a standard problem of combinatorial analysis [158], [199]. We have $P(0) = 1$ since there is only one way of writing zero as a nonnegative integer linear combination of positive roots. Setting $\lambda = 0$ into the Kostant formula, we obtain the following recursion relation, valid for $\mu \neq 0$:

$$P(\mu) = - \sum_{\substack{w \in W \\ w \neq 1}} (\det w) P[\mu - \delta + w\delta].$$

This recursion relation can be used as a method for computing the partition function. Tarski used this method to compute by hand the partition function for the algebras A_2, B_2, G_2 and A_3, but the formulas became very involved [226]. A computer implementation of the Kostant formula has been reported [25].

Racah [196] suggested another formula for characters and this method has also been described by Klimyk [140]. The Racah formula provides a recursion relation directly for the multiplicities of the weights:

$$n_\mu = - \sum_{\substack{w \in W \\ w \neq 1}} (\det w) n_{\mu + \delta - w\delta}.$$

It does not involve the partition function. A computer implementation of this formula has also been reported [25].

3.14 THE STEINBERG AND RACAH FORMULAS FOR CLEBSCH–GORDAN SERIES

One of the main applications of characters is to reduce tensor products of irreducible modules over a semisimple Lie algebra, that is, to calculate the Clebsch–Gordan series. Suppose we want to reduce the tensor product $M_1 \otimes M_2$ of irreducible modules M_1 and M_2 having highest weights λ_1 and λ_2 respectively. The *outer multiplicity* $m^\lambda{}_{\lambda_1 \lambda_2}$ of a linear form $\lambda \in J$ is the number of irreducible submodules with highest weight λ occurring in the Clebsch–Gordan series for the tensor product $M_1 \otimes M_2$. These outer multiplicities can be computed from the characters by the formula

$$\chi_{\lambda_1} \chi_{\lambda_2} = \sum_{\lambda \in J} m^\lambda{}_{\lambda_1 \lambda_2} \chi_\lambda.$$

Given the weight diagrams, this formula could be used directly to compute the outer multiplicities by a process of repeated subtraction. The leading term on the right is the one for

$$\lambda = \lambda_1 + \lambda_2,$$

and by examining the coefficient of $e^{\lambda_1 + \lambda_2}$, we see that

$$m^{\lambda_1 + \lambda_2}_{\lambda_1 \lambda_2} = 1.$$

Subtracting this term from both sides and examining the leading terms of the remaining expression yields the outer multiplicity of the next highest submodule, and so on. This procedure can easily be programmed for a computing machine, and thus each method for computing weight diagrams yields a corresponding method for computing Clebsch–Gordan series. In practice, this procedure for computing the outer multiplicities can be made more efficient [140], [155]. For example, if the Weyl girdle method is chosen, only one girdle division is needed if we rewrite the above formula as

$$\xi_{\lambda_1} \xi_{\lambda_2} / \xi_0 = \sum_{\lambda \in J} m^\lambda{}_{\lambda_1 \lambda_2} \xi_\lambda.$$

Steinberg used the Kostant formula to develop a method for calculating these Clebsch–Gordan series directly [219]. The *Steinberg formula* for $m^\lambda{}_{\lambda_1\lambda_2}$ involves a double summation over the Weyl group:

$$m^\lambda{}_{\lambda_1\lambda_2} = \sum_{v,w\in W} (\det vw)P[v(\lambda_1 + \delta) + w(\lambda_2 + \delta) - (\lambda + 2\delta)].$$

Some applications of the Steinberg formula have been given in the literature [198], [221], [222].

The Steinberg formula is a generalization of the original Clebsch–Gordan formula for computing the tensor product of modules over the simple Lie algebra A_1. The character of the irreducible module M_λ with spin j, highest weight $\lambda = j\alpha$, and dimension $2j + 1$ is

$$\chi_\lambda = e^{j\alpha} + e^{(j-1)\alpha} + \cdots + e^{-j\alpha} = \sum_{m=-j}^{j} e^{m\alpha}.$$

We may use this character formula directly to reduce the tensor product $M_\lambda \otimes M_{\lambda'}$ of two such modules as a direct sum of irreducible submodules. Setting $\lambda = j\alpha$ and $\lambda' = j'\alpha$, we find that the character of the tensor product module is

$$\chi_{j\alpha}\chi_{j'\alpha} = \left(\sum_{m=-j}^{j} e^{m\alpha}\right)\left(\sum_{m'=-j'}^{j'} e^{m'\alpha}\right) = \sum_{j''=|j-j'|}^{j+j'} \chi_{j''\alpha}.$$

The Clebsch–Gordan series for A_1 are thus given by

$$M_{j\alpha} \otimes M_{j'\alpha} \approx \bigoplus_{j''=|j-j'|}^{j+j'} M_{j''\alpha},$$

a familiar result in angular momentum theory [203]. These results follow immediately from the Steinberg formula. Since the Weyl group of A_1 has two elements, 1 and w, the Steinberg formula has four terms only. We may set $\lambda = j\alpha$, $\lambda_1 = j_1\alpha$ and $\lambda_2 = j_2\alpha$, and note that $\delta = \alpha/2$ and $w\mu = -\mu$ for any weight μ. Thus the Steinberg formula reduces to

$$m^\lambda{}_{\lambda_1\lambda_2} = P[(j_1 + j_2 - j)\alpha] - P[(j_1 - j_2 - j - 1)\alpha]$$
$$- P[(j_2 - j_1 - j - 1)\alpha] + P[-(j_1 + j_2 + j + 2)\alpha].$$

For A_1, the partition function $P(\mu)$ is unity if $\mu = n\alpha$, where n is an integer ≥ 0, and zero otherwise. Clearly $m^\lambda{}_{\lambda_1\lambda_2} = 0$ unless $j_1 + j_2 - j$ is an integer. Since $j_1 \geq 0$, $j_2 \geq 0$ and $0 \leq j \leq j_1 + j_2$, the last term in the Steinberg formula is always zero. Of the two terms with negative signs, only one can contribute at a time, and it does so when $|j_1 - j_2| > j$, canceling out the contribution from the first term on the right. Thus we find that $m^\lambda{}_{\lambda_1\lambda_2} = 1$ when $j_1 + j_2 - j$ is an integer and $|j_1 - j_2| \leq j \leq j_1 + j_2$, while $m^\lambda{}_{\lambda_1\lambda_2} = 0$ otherwise.

We shall also illustrate the use of the Steinberg formula for the simple Lie algebra A_2, corresponding to the group $SU(3)$. The Cartan matrix of A_2 is

$$\begin{bmatrix} 2 & -1 \\ -1 & 2 \end{bmatrix},$$

and its inverse is

$$\begin{bmatrix} 2/3 & 1/3 \\ 1/3 & 2/3 \end{bmatrix}.$$

Hence the basic weights λ_1 and λ_2 are related to the simple roots α_1 and α_2 by

$$\lambda_1 = (2\alpha_1 + \alpha_2)/3, \qquad \lambda_2 = (\alpha_1 + 2\alpha_2)/3.$$

From the root system, shown in Fig. 4 (§ 2.15), we see that α_1, α_2 and $\alpha_1 + \alpha_2$ are the positive roots.

Using the Weyl formula, we find that the dimension of an irreducible module with highest weight $p\lambda_1 + q\lambda_2$ is given by

$$\dim M = \tfrac{1}{2}(p + 1)(q + 1)(p + q + 1).$$

In particular,

$$\dim M_{\lambda_1} = \dim M_{\lambda_2} = 3$$

and

$$\dim M_0 = 1, \qquad \dim M_{\lambda_1 + \lambda_2} = 8,$$

so that we may write

$$M_0 = \{\mathbf{1}\}, \quad M_{\lambda_1} = \{\mathbf{3}\}, \quad M_{\lambda_2} = \{\mathbf{3^*}\} \quad \text{and} \quad M_{\lambda_1 + \lambda_2} = \{\mathbf{8}\}.$$

We now show by means of the Steinberg formula that

$$M_{\lambda_1} \otimes M_{\lambda_2} \approx M_0 \dotplus M_{\lambda_1 + \lambda_2},$$

or in other words,

$$\{\mathbf{3}\} \otimes \{\mathbf{3^*}\} \approx \{\mathbf{1}\} \dotplus \{\mathbf{8}\}.$$

To apply the Steinberg formula, of course, we need to use the Weyl group. The Weyl group W of the simple Lie algebra A_2 consists of the elements 1, w_1, w_2, w_1w_2, w_2w_1 and $w_1w_2w_1 = w_2w_1w_2$. This group is isomorphic to the symmetric group S_3 of all permutations on three elements, the correspondence being given by

$$1 \leftrightarrow e, \qquad\qquad w_1w_2 \leftrightarrow (123),$$

$$w_1 \leftrightarrow (23), \qquad\qquad w_2w_1 \leftrightarrow (132),$$

$$w_2 \leftrightarrow (13), \qquad w_1w_2w_1 \leftrightarrow (12).$$

The action of the Weyl group on the positive roots is shown in Fig. 14.

	α_1	α_2	$\alpha_1 + \alpha_2$
1	α_1	α_2	$\alpha_1 + \alpha_2$
w_1	$-\alpha_1$	$\alpha_1 + \alpha_2$	α_2
w_2	$\alpha_1 + \alpha_2$	$-\alpha_2$	α_1
$w_1 w_2$	α_2	$-(\alpha_1 + \alpha_2)$	$-\alpha_1$
$w_2 w_1$	$-(\alpha_1 + \alpha_2)$	α_1	$-\alpha_2$
$w_1 w_2 w_1$	$-\alpha_2$	$-\alpha_1$	$-(\alpha_1 + \alpha_2)$

FIG. 14. *Action of Weyl group on positive roots* $\alpha_1, \alpha_2, \alpha_1 + \alpha_2$ *of* A_2

By looking at dimensions, the only candidates for submodules in the reduction of $\{3\} \otimes \{3^*\}$ are $\{1\}$ and $\{8\}$, and possibly also the modules $\{6\} = M_{2\lambda_1}$ and $\{6^*\} = M_{2\lambda_2}$. Using the Steinberg formula, we find that the multiplicity of the module with highest weight 0 for example is

$$m^0_{\lambda_1 \lambda_2} = P(\alpha_1 + \alpha_2) - P(\alpha_1) - P(\alpha_2) + P(0)$$

$$= 2 - 1 - 1 + 1 = 1.$$

Similarly, the multiplicity of the module with highest weight $\lambda_1 + \lambda_2$ is also 1, so that indeed

$$\{3\} \otimes \{3^*\} \approx \{1\} \dotplus \{8\}.$$

These results could also have been obtained by other means, besides the Steinberg formula. For this Lie algebra, and more generally also for the simple Lie algebras of types A–D, there are some frequently used alternative methods involving Young tableaux for computing Clebsch–Gordan series [115].

Another formula for computing Clebsch–Gordan series is due to Racah. It is a recursive formula which avoids the partition function and the double summation over the Weyl group, but does require the computation of the weight diagram of the module M_1 with highest weight λ_1. *Racah's formula* is

$$m^\lambda_{\lambda_1 \lambda_2} = \sum_{w \in W} (\det w) n_{\lambda + \delta - w(\lambda_2 + \delta)},$$

where $n_{\lambda + \delta - w(\lambda_2 + \delta)}$ is the multiplicity of the weight $\lambda + \delta - w(\lambda_2 + \delta)$ in the module M_1 with highest weight λ_1.

3.15 TENSOR ANALYSIS

We shall now turn to the explicit construction of modules over simple Lie algebras, using tensor analysis. The classical methods of tensor analysis, suitably modernized, are useful for such practical matters as computing Clebsch–Gordan and Racah coefficients, which are much used in applications. The degree of difficulty of such computations frequently depends on the availability of suitable methods to construct the irreducible modules, and some flexibility in this respect is often welcome. For this reason, the knowledge of several different ways to construct a particular irreducible module is not a useless luxury. The classical procedure is to try to generate all the irreducible modules from some particular one. By taking tensor powers of this particular module, and applying such processes as symmetrization and contraction, one may hope to construct all the other irreducible modules. This leads us to study the general classification of tensors according to their symmetry properties and degree of tracelessness.

The construction of all modules has been pushed back from general modules to irreducible modules by means of direct sum decompositions and from irreducible modules to basic modules by means of the Cartan composition. By the use of tensor analysis, we can continue this process back one more step, arriving finally at the concept of an *elementary module* [83], [216]. An elementary module is a basic module corresponding to a terminal node of the Dynkin diagram. It is a module from which we can generate the other basic modules by tensorial methods. The elementary modules are thus the natural building blocks out of which to construct all possible modules.

We shall begin our discussion of tensor analysis by considering Lie algebras of type A_l because this is the simplest case. The basic modules for these algebras are specified by their highest weights as shown in the Dynkin diagrams in Fig. 15.

Module	Highest weight	Dynkin diagram
M_1	λ_1	1 0 0 . . . 0
M_2	λ_2	0 1 0 . . . 0
M_3	λ_3	0 0 1 . . . 0
⋮	⋮	⋮
M_l	λ_l	0 0 0 . . . 1

FIG. 15. *Basic modules for the simple Lie algebra* A_l

The simple Lie algebra A_l may be identified with the linear Lie algebra consisting of all traceless linear operators in an $(l + 1)$-dimensional vector space M over the complex number field. The vector space M may itself be regarded as an irreducible module with highest weight λ_1, and may thus be identified with the basic module M_1. The module M is an elementary module over the simple Lie algebra A_l, and the other basic modules M_2, $M_3, \cdots, M_l$ can be constructed as exterior powers of M. Explicitly, the basic module M_k is isomorphic to the kth exterior power of the elementary module:

$$M_k \approx \wedge^k M = M \wedge \cdots \wedge M \quad (k \text{ copies}).$$

One could equally well construct all modules starting with the dual module $M^* \approx M_l$, so that the dual module M^* may also be regarded as an elementary module.

Similar procedures can be applied, with varying degrees of success, for the simple Lie algebras B_l, C_l and D_l. For these algebras, a natural module to use as a building block would be the one whose Dynkin diagram is listed in Fig. 16.

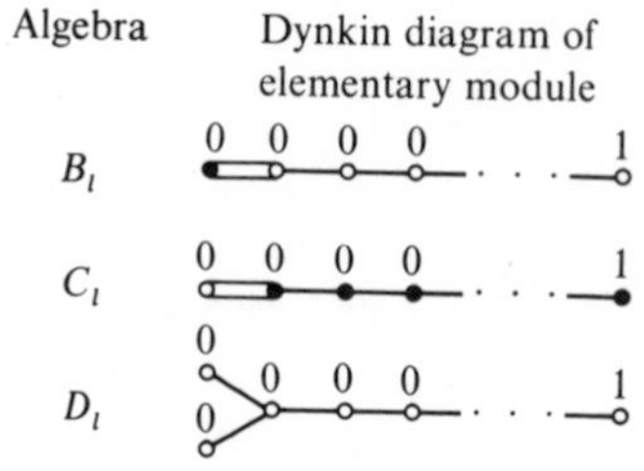

FIG. 16. *Elementary modules for tensor analysis in the simple Lie algebras B_l, C_l, D_l*

For the orthogonal algebras B_l and D_l, the exterior powers $\wedge^k M$ again yield all but one or two of the basic modules. The omitted modules are the basic spinor module of B_l and the two basic semispinor modules of D_l, which we shall discuss later. For the symplectic Lie algebras C_l, the exterior powers $\wedge^k M$ are not irreducible, and to obtain the basic modules this method must be supplemented by a trace removal process.

3.16 YOUNG TABLEAUX

Once the basic modules have been constructed from the elementary ones, we can then construct all irreducible modules via Cartan composition, making use of the enveloping algebra. In this way, in principle, the entire representation theory is reduced to a single elementary module. For some applications it is advantageous to bypass the Cartan composition procedure and construct the irreducible modules directly from the elementary module via tensor analysis. To do this, one needs to study the symmetrization of the tensor powers of the elementary module M. We consider here the case of algebras of type A_l for which this procedure is fairly straightforward [115], [131]. The tensor power module $\bigotimes^n M$ may be considered not only as a module over the Lie algebra A_l, but also as a module over the permutation group S_n. For each permutation π in S_n, there is a linear operator on the tensor power module $\bigotimes^n M$ which permutes the various factors in the tensor product. We define the action of π on the tensor product of the vectors $x_1, \cdots, x_n$ in M by

$$\pi(x_1 \otimes \cdots \otimes x_n) = x_{\pi(1)} \otimes \cdots \otimes x_{\pi(n)}.$$

The idea now is to construct projection operators by using the group algebra of the permutation group, making use of the theory of Young tableaux [204]. (The latter will be defined below.) For example, if δ_π denotes the parity factor ± 1 of the permutation π, we can define an antisymmetrizer in the group algebra by

$$\mathscr{A} = \sum_{\pi \in S_n} \delta_\pi \cdot \pi.$$

The exterior power $\wedge^n M$ is then naturally isomorphic to the antisymmetric submodule $\mathscr{A} \bigotimes^n M$ of the tensor power.

To go further one uses some results from the Wedderburn theory of semisimple associative algebras. In addition to the antisymmetrizer, we can construct other operators which project irreducible components out of the tensor powers of the elementary module. There is in fact a basis e_{ij}^α for the group algebra of the permutation group S_n satisfying

$$e_{ij}^\alpha e_{kl}^\beta = \delta^{\alpha\beta} \delta_{jk} e_{il}^\alpha.$$

For a given α, the elements e_{ij}^α generate a simple ideal of the associative group algebra of the permutation group. The elements $e_r^\alpha = e_{rr}^\alpha$ are seen to be projection operators, $(e_r^\alpha)^2 = e_r^\alpha$, and give a resolution of the unity element of the group algebra:

$$1 = \sum_{\alpha, r} e_r^\alpha.$$

The ideals of the group algebra of the permutation group can be labeled by means of Young shapes as follows. A *partition* $[\alpha]$ of an integer n is a list of integers $[\alpha_1, \cdots, \alpha_k]$ such that $\alpha_1 \geq \alpha_2 \geq \cdots \geq \alpha_k > 0$ and

$$\alpha_1 + \cdots + \alpha_k = n.$$

The partition $[\alpha]$ can be denoted by a *Young shape* consisting of n boxes arranged so that α_j boxes occur in the jth row. If there are several α's which are equal, then we may use an abbreviated notation, where α^m means that α is repeated m times. For example, the partition $[2^2 1]$ is represented by the Young shape

A *Young tableau* is a Young shape in which the boxes have been numbered from 1, $\cdots$, n in some order. A *standard Young tableau* is a tableau with the property that if all but the boxes labeled 1, $\cdots$, h with $h < n$ are erased, then these remaining h boxes form a Young tableau by themselves. An example of a standard Young tableau is

1	3
2	5
4	

The number f_α of standard Young tableaux for a given Young shape $[\alpha]$ = $[\alpha_1, \cdots, \alpha_k]$ is

$$f_\alpha = \frac{n! \prod_{i<j\leq k} (x_i - x_j)}{\prod_i x_i!},$$

where $x_i = \alpha_i + k - i$. The standard Young tableaux corresponding to a given shape $[\alpha]$ can be labeled $[\alpha]_r$, where r runs from 1 to f_α. The particular method of numbering the standard tableaux is a matter of convention.

The theory of Young tableaux leads to an explicit construction for the basis elements e_{ij}^α of the group algebra of the permutation group S_n. To carry out this construction one defines, for each Young tableau $[\alpha]_r$, a pair of subgroups called the positive and negative groups. The *positive group* $P[\alpha]_r$ contains all permutations which permute only the numbers within each row, while the *negative group* $N[\alpha]_r$ contains all permutations which permute only numbers within each column of the tableau. For example, the permutation (13) (25) belongs to the positive group of the standard tableau given in our example, while (124) belongs to the negative group. We define a *symmetrizer* P_r^α, which is the sum of all the elements of the positive group, and an *antisymmetrizer* N_r^α, equal to the sum of all elements of the negative group, each element being multiplied by its parity sign factor. Explicitly, the symmetrizer on all the elements in rows of the tableau is given by

$$P_r^\alpha = \sum_{\pi \in P[\alpha]_r} \pi,$$

and the antisymmetrizer on the columns of the tableau is given by

$$N_r^\alpha = \sum_{\pi \in N[\alpha]_r} \delta_\pi \cdot \pi.$$

Let σ_{rs}^α denote the permutation which transforms the tableau $[\alpha]_s$ into the tableau $[\alpha]_r$:

$$[\alpha]_r = \sigma_{rs}^\alpha [\alpha]_s,$$

and define

$$E_{rs}^\alpha = P_r^\alpha \sigma_{rs}^\alpha N_s^\alpha.$$

The elements E_{rs}^α form a basis for the group algebra of the permutation group, but do not have simple multiplication laws. To obtain simpler basis elements, we first expand E_{rs}^α in terms of all the permutations π in S_n:

$$E_{rs}^\alpha = \sum_{\pi \in S_n} \zeta_{rs}^\alpha(\pi) \cdot \pi,$$

and we denote by ζ_{rs}^α the coefficient of the identity permutation e in this expansion

$$\zeta_{rs}^\alpha = \zeta_{rs}^\alpha(e).$$

Let $(\zeta^\alpha)^{-1} = \eta^\alpha$ denote the matrix inverse to the matrix whose elements are the coefficients ζ_{rs}^α. Then the elements

$$e_{rs}^\alpha = \frac{f_\alpha}{n!} \sum_t E_{rt}^\alpha \eta_{ts}^\alpha$$

form a basis of the group algebra of the permutation group, and these have the simple multiplication properties mentioned earlier. It turns out that the matrix η^α is in fact very close to being a unit matrix, and for the elements with $r = s$, with which we are primarily concerned here, these coefficients effectively disappear, and we have simply

$$e_r^\alpha = e_{rr}^\alpha = \frac{f_\alpha}{n!} E_{rr}^\alpha = \frac{f_\alpha}{n!} P_r^\alpha N_r^\alpha.$$

Thus the projection operators can be computed directly from the positive and negative groups of the tableau, without requiring a calculation of the η_{rs}^α coefficients [204].

    The permutations π in S_n commute with the elements x in the Lie algebra and hence so do the elements e_r^α, from which it follows immediately that $e_r^\alpha M^n$ is a submodule of the module M^n. The modules $e_r^\alpha M^n$ for the same Young shape α, but different tableaux r and s, are isomorphic:

$$e_r^\alpha M^n \approx e_s^\alpha M^n.$$

For algebras of type A_l, these modules are all irreducible, and each irreducible module can be obtained in this way by projecting out symmetrized portions of the tensor powers of the elementary module [244]. In general, however, there will be infinitely many different Young shapes corresponding to a given irreducible module. To obtain a one-to-one correspondence between isomorphism classes of irreducible modules and Young shapes for Lie algebras of type A_l, we may restrict the class of Young shapes under consideration to those with at most l rows. The irreducible modules can then be characterized either by such a restricted Young shape $[\alpha]$ or by the highest weight λ. For a Young shape $[\alpha] = [\alpha_1, \cdots, \alpha_k]$ with a total of n boxes, the highest weight of the modules $e_r^\alpha M^n$ is

$$\lambda = \sum_{i=1}^{k} (\alpha_i - \alpha_{i+1})\lambda_i,$$

where $\lambda_1, \cdots, \lambda_l$ are the basic weights and we set $\alpha_{l+1} = 0$. Since the projection operators e_r^α form a resolution of the identity, we also have

$$M^n = \bigoplus_{\alpha, r} e_r^\alpha M^n,$$

giving a complete reduction of the tensor powers of the elementary module into its irreducible components. This is equivalent to the classical reduction of a tensor with an arbitrary number of indices to a sum of tensors with definite symmetry properties.

3.17 CONTRACTIONS

For Lie algebras of types B_l, C_l and D_l, the reduction of the tensor powers of a module M into symmetrized tensor powers $e_r^\alpha M^n$ is not complete because these submodules need not be irreducible [6]. To remedy this, we need to discuss the process of contraction of tensors and the removal of traces [195].

For the module M we shall take the space traditionally used to define the algebras B_l, C_l and D_l. It has $2l + 1$ dimensions for the odd-type orthogonal Lie algebras B_l, and it has $2l$ dimensions for both the even-type orthogonal Lie algebras D_l and the symplectic Lie algebras C_l. The defining module M is equipped with a nonsingular bilinear form (x, y) which is symmetric in the case of the orthogonal Lie algebras and antisymmetric for the symplectic Lie algebras. In both cases, the Lie algebra elements $a \in L$ are linear operators on M which are antisymmetric with respect to the bilinear form

$$(ax, y) = -(x, ay).$$

For $i, j = 1, \cdots, n$ we define the *contraction operator*

$$c_{ij} : M^n \to M^{n-2}$$

by

$$c_{ij}(x_1 \otimes \cdots \otimes x_n) = (x_i, x_j) \cdot x_1 \otimes \cdots \hat{x}_i \cdots \hat{x}_j \cdots \otimes x_n.$$

A circumflex is used here to indicate that the corresponding factor is to be omitted. The contraction operators are easily seen to commute with all elements of the Lie algebra. The induced bilinear form on M^n, defined by

$$(x_1 \otimes \cdots \otimes x_n, y_1 \otimes \cdots \otimes y_n) = (x_1, y_1) \cdots (x_n, y_n),$$

allows us to talk about orthogonality for tensors. One can now classify tensors according to their degree of tracelessness, and thus arrive at the orthogonal direct sum decomposition

$$M^n = \bigoplus_{k=0}^{[n/2]} M_k^n.$$

Here M_1^n consists of completely traceless tensors, that is, elements of M^n which are annihilated by any contraction. The space M_2^n consists of tensors which are orthogonal to all traceless tensors but which are annihilated by a product of any two contractions and so forth, producing spaces M_k^n which are mutually orthogonal and linearly independent. Finally, the remainder, if any, is the subspace M_0^n orthogonal to all of the subspaces M_k^n with $k = 1, 2, \cdots, [n/2]$, which therefore consists of those tensors most resistant against being annihilated by contractions.

As an example of such a decomposition into traceless tensors we may consider an orthogonal Lie algebra. In the module M we may introduce an orthonormal basis $e_1, \cdots, e_n$ satisfying

$$(e_i, e_j) = \delta_{ij}.$$

The tensor product module $M^2 = M \otimes M$ may then be decomposed as

$$M^2 = M_0^2 \oplus M_1^2,$$

where M_0^2 is spanned by the single tensor $\sum_{i=1}^n e_i \otimes e_i$, and M_1^2 is spanned by the tensors $e_i \otimes e_j$ and $e_i \otimes e_i - e_j \otimes e_j$, where $i \neq j$.

The submodules M_k^n of the tensor power M^n are not yet irreducible in general, but since they are modules over the permutation group S_n as well as over the Lie algebra, we may carry out a further reduction by symmetrization. The submodules $e_r^\alpha M_k^n$ are finally irreducible modules over the Lie algebra, but they are not all distinct, and there are various isomorphisms between these modules [115]. In addition, for the orthogonal-type Lie algebras there exist modules which can only be obtained by supplementing the methods of tensor analysis with the methods of spinor analysis.

For the symplectic Lie algebras C_l, the exterior powers $\wedge^n M$ of the defining module M fail to be irreducible, and the contraction process enters into the construction of the basic modules. As a typical example, we shall study the case of the simple Lie algebra C_3. The Lie algebra C_3 is related to the symplectic Lie group $Sp(3)$, which may be considered as a group of 6×6 complex matrices, and therefore the 6-dimensional basic irreducible module appears to be a natural starting point for building up the others. The Dynkin diagrams of this module and of the other two basic modules, as well as of some other modules, are shown in Fig. 17.

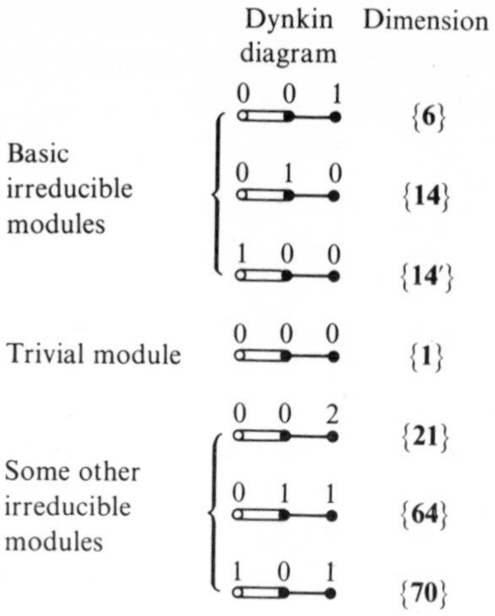

Dynkin   Dimension
diagram

Basic
irreducible
modules

$$\begin{array}{ccc} 0 & 0 & 1 \end{array}$$ {6}

$$\begin{array}{ccc} 0 & 1 & 0 \end{array}$$ {14}

$$\begin{array}{ccc} 1 & 0 & 0 \end{array}$$ {14'}

Trivial module $$\begin{array}{ccc} 0 & 0 & 0 \end{array}$$ {1}

Some other
irreducible
modules

$$\begin{array}{ccc} 0 & 0 & 2 \end{array}$$ {21}

$$\begin{array}{ccc} 0 & 1 & 1 \end{array}$$ {64}

$$\begin{array}{ccc} 1 & 0 & 1 \end{array}$$ {70}

FIG. 17. *Dynkin diagrams for some of the irreducible modules for the Lie algebra* C_3

The Dynkin diagrams for the complete weight system of the fundamental 6-dimensional module and the simple roots of C_3 are given in Fig. 18. The weight system here was calculated by using the Dynkin algorithm discussed earlier (§ 3.8).

The following Clebsch–Gordan series of modules over C_3 can be obtained, for instance, from a study of characters:

$$\{6\} \otimes \{6\} \approx \{1\} \dotplus \{14\} \dotplus \{21\},$$

$$\{6\} \otimes \{14\} \approx \{6\} \dotplus \{14'\} \dotplus \{64\},$$

$$\{6\} \otimes \{14'\} \approx \{14\} \dotplus \{70\}.$$

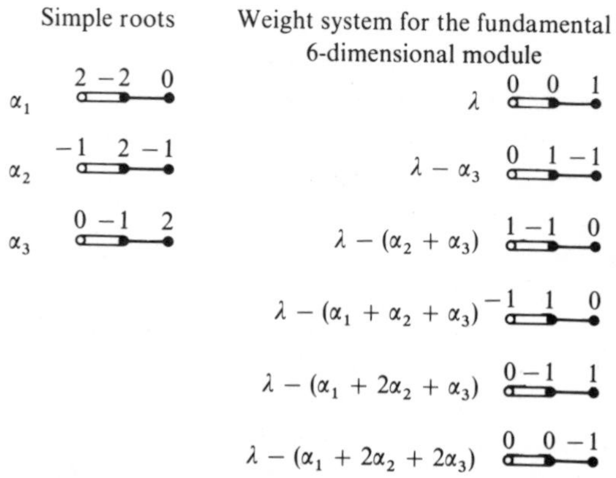

Simple roots   Weight system for the fundamental 6-dimensional module

α_1 $\begin{array}{ccc} 2 & -2 & 0 \end{array}$ λ $\begin{array}{ccc} 0 & 0 & 1 \end{array}$

α_2 $\begin{array}{ccc} -1 & 2 & -1 \end{array}$ $\lambda - \alpha_3$ $\begin{array}{ccc} 0 & 1 & -1 \end{array}$

α_3 $\begin{array}{ccc} 0 & -1 & 2 \end{array}$ $\lambda - (\alpha_2 + \alpha_3)$ $\begin{array}{ccc} 1 & -1 & 0 \end{array}$

$\lambda - (\alpha_1 + \alpha_2 + \alpha_3)$ $\begin{array}{ccc} -1 & 1 & 0 \end{array}$

$\lambda - (\alpha_1 + 2\alpha_2 + \alpha_3)$ $\begin{array}{ccc} 0 & -1 & 1 \end{array}$

$\lambda - (\alpha_1 + 2\alpha_2 + 2\alpha_3)$ $\begin{array}{ccc} 0 & 0 & -1 \end{array}$

FIG. 18. *Roots and fundamental weights for the simple Lie algebra* C_3

The Dynkin diagrams for the various modules which appear here are among those included in Fig. 17.

The decomposition of the antisymmetrized tensor powers can now be written down by inspection of the dimensions involved. The module $\{6\} \otimes \{6\}$ is a 36-dimensional vector space, which breaks up into a symmetric part with $(6 \times 7)/(1 \times 2) = 21$ dimensions and an antisymmetric part with $(5 \times 6)/(1 \times 2) = 15$ dimensions. From these dimensional considerations and the Clebsch–Gordan series decomposition given previously, it is clear that the decomposition of the antisymmetric part is given by

$$\wedge^2\{6\} = \{6\} \wedge \{6\} \approx \{1\} \dotplus \{14\}.$$

The antisymmetrized cube $\wedge^3\{6\}$ of the fundamental module is contained in

$$\{6\} \otimes \wedge^2\{6\} \approx \{6\} \dotplus \{6\} \dotplus \{14'\} \dotplus \{64\}.$$

Since its dimension is $(4 \times 5 \times 6)/(1 \times 2 \times 3) = 20$, its decomposition can only be given by

$$\wedge^3\{6\} = \{6\} \wedge \{6\} \wedge \{6\} \approx \{6\} \dotplus \{14'\}.$$

By similar use of dimension counting and Clebsch–Gordan series, the remaining antisymmetrized tensor powers of the fundamental module are found to be given by

$$\wedge^4\{6\} \approx \{1\} \dotplus \{14\}, \quad \wedge^5\{6\} \approx \{6\}, \quad \wedge^6\{6\} \approx \{1\},$$

and all higher powers are zero. From this we see that the basic modules of C_3 can still be constructed from the exterior powers of the fundamental module M, but some additional process must be used to separate off the accompanying one- and six-dimensional modules.

3.18 SPINOR ANALYSIS AND CLIFFORD ALGEBRAS

The defining module M of an orthogonal Lie algebra can be used to construct all of the basic modules except the spinor and semispinor modules. Thus for the constructive representation theory of these algebras, we must supplement the methods of tensor analysis with those of spinor analysis. To complete the picture, we now discuss these basic spinor and semispinor modules over the orthogonal Lie algebras. For simple Lie algebras of type B_l, there is a single basic spinor module, while for simple Lie algebras of type D_l, there are two basic semispinor modules. The Dynkin diagrams of the basic spinor and semispinor modules are given in Fig. 19.

Spinors were first discovered by Cartan in 1913 as a byproduct of his classification of all simple Lie groups. Later, these spinor representations became famous in the special case of the Lie algebra $A_1 \approx B_1$ through their role in the Pauli theory of electron spin. To construct the spinor modules,

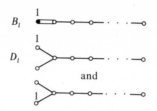

FIG. 19. *Dynkin diagrams for the basic spinor and semispinor modules over orthogonal Lie algebras B_l and D_l*

we introduce the Clifford algebra of the defining module M of the orthogonal Lie algebra L. This module M may be regarded as a module over the group $SO(n, \mathbb{R})$ or over the corresponding complex Lie algebra L. We recall that M is an n-dimensional complex vector space equipped with a nonsingular symmetric bilinear form (x, y). The orthogonal Lie algebra L is the complex Lie algebra of linear operators on M which are antisymmetric with respect to this bilinear form. If n is an odd integer, $n = 2l + 1$ with $l \geq 1$, then L is B_l, and if n is an even integer, $n = 2l$ with $l \geq 1$, then L is D_l.

Clifford algebras were originally discovered as generalizations of quaternions [62]. The Clifford algebra related to the Lorentz group $SO(3, 1; \mathbb{R})$ is the Dirac gamma algebra, which is widely used today in relativistic quantum mechanics [103], [188]. Since Clifford algebras are determined abstractly by their generators and relations, we may construct them explicitly via tensor algebras [56]. Let K be the ideal in the tensor algebra $T(M)$ over the module M generated by all elements of the form

$$z \otimes z - (z, z)1,$$

where $z \in M$. The quotient algebra

$$C(M) = T(M)/K$$

is an associative algebra with unity called the *first Clifford algebra* of the module M with respect to the bilinear form (x, y). Since the composition of the canonical mapping of $T(M)$ onto $C(M)$ with the inclusion mapping of M into $T(M)$ yields a one-to-one mapping, we may identify M with its image in $C(M)$. The Clifford algebra $C(M)$ obtained in this way satisfies the following universality property. If A is an associative algebra with unity, then any linear mapping $\gamma : M \to A$ which satisfies

$$\gamma(z)^2 = (z, z)1$$

can be extended to a unique homomorphism from $C(M)$ into A.

To study the properties of the Clifford algebra, it is convenient to describe the algebra in terms of generators and relations. Denoting the product in $C(M)$ of elements x and y in M by xy, we have the *Jordan relations*

$$xy + yx = 2(x, y) \cdot 1$$

for all x, $y \in M$. The generators and relations for a Clifford algebra take the especially simple form

$$x_i x_j + x_j x_i = 2\delta_{ij}1$$

if we introduce an orthonormal basis $x_1, \cdots, x_n$ in M. We can then show that the dimension of the first Clifford algebra is given by $\dim C(M) = 2^n$ since $x_1^{r_1} \cdots x_n^{r_n}$, where $r_i = 0, 1$, is a basis for the Clifford algebra.

We may note that the Jordan relations are invariant under replacement of all vectors in M by their negatives. Consequently, the mapping $z \mapsto -z$ in M induces an involutive automorphism of the Clifford algebra $C(M)$. Denoting the image of an element $t \in C(M)$ under this automorphism by t^*, we have $t^{**} = t$, and $z^* = -z$ for all $z \in M$. If we split $C(M)$ into two parts corresponding to the eigenvalues ± 1 of this automorphism, then the part $C^+(M)$ corresponding to the eigenvalue $+1$ is a subalgebra of $C(M)$ called the *second Clifford algebra* [10].

We can clarify the structures of the first and second Clifford algebras somewhat as follows. For each vector $z \in M$, we introduce a linear operator $\alpha(z)$ on $C(M)$ by

$$\alpha(z)t = zt + t^*z.$$

By direct computation, one verifies that these operators anticommute, that is, they satisfy

$$\alpha(z)\alpha(z') = -\alpha(z')\alpha(z)$$

for all z, $z' \in M$. If we let M_k be the subspace of $C(M)$ spanned by all elements of the form $\alpha(z_1) \cdots \alpha(z_k) \cdot 1$, then

$$C(M) = M_0 \oplus M_1 \oplus \cdots \oplus M_n.$$

In particular, we note that

$$\alpha(z_1) \cdot 1 = 2z_1,$$

$$\alpha(z_1)\alpha(z_2) \cdot 1 = 2[z_1, z_2],$$

and hence,

$$M_0 = \mathbb{C}, \quad M_1 = M \quad \text{and} \quad M_2 = [M, M].$$

Since the operators $\alpha(z_i)$ anticommute, the expression $\alpha(z_1) \cdots \alpha(z_k) \cdot 1$ is completely antisymmetric in the vectors $z_1, \cdots, z_k$. The mapping $z_1 \wedge \cdots \wedge z_k \mapsto \alpha(z_1) \cdots \alpha(z_k) \cdot 1$ establishes a vector-space isomorphism between the exterior power $\wedge^k M$ and the subspace M_k, and hence $\dim M^k = \binom{n}{k}$. Since

$$t = \alpha(z_1) \cdots \alpha(z_k) \cdot 1$$

satisfies $t^* = (-1)^k t$, it should be apparent that the second Clifford algebra is given by

$$C^+(M) = M_0 \oplus M_2 \oplus M_4 \oplus \cdots.$$

In other words, the second Clifford algebra is spanned by the even elements of the first Clifford algebra, and it follows that it is a subalgebra with $\dim C^+(M) = 2^{n-1}$.

For example, the first Clifford algebra for the Lie algebra $A_1 \approx B_1$ corresponding to the ordinary rotation group $SO(3, \mathbb{R})$ is generated by three elements x_1, x_2 and x_3 satisfying the Jordan relations. In this case, the first Clifford algebra $C(M)$ is an eight-dimensional algebra spanned by the elements $1, x_1, x_2, x_3, x_1 x_2, x_2 x_3, x_1 x_3$ and $x_1 x_2 x_3$. The second Clifford algebra $C^+(M)$ is the four-dimensional subalgebra of $C(M)$ spanned by $1, i = x_1 x_3, j = x_2 x_3$ and $k = x_3 x_1$. Since i, j and k satisfy $i^2 = j^2 = k^2 = -1$, and $ij = -ji = k$, $jk = -kj = i$, and $ki = ik = j$, we may identify $C^+(M)$ as the complex quaternion algebra.

Since the Clifford algebra $C(M)$ is an associative algebra, we may also regard it as a Lie algebra $C(M)_L$ under commutation. To see that the Lie algebra L itself may be regarded as a subalgebra of the Lie algebra $C(M)_L$, we argue as follows. For all x, y and z in M we may obtain the relation

$$[[x, y], z] = 4(y, z)x - 4(x, z)y$$

from the Jordan relation by writing the term $4(y, z)x$ on the right-hand side, for instance, as

$$(yz + zy)x + x(yz + zy).$$

An immediate corollary of this formula is that

$$[M_2, M] \subset M,$$

and hence, we also find

$$[M_2, M_2] = [M_2, [M, M]] \subset [[M_2, M], M] \subset [M, M] = M_2$$

by using the Jacobi identity. Hence, M_2 is a subalgebra of the Lie algebra $C(M)_L$, and we shall argue that $M_2 \approx L$. For each $a \in M_2$, if we define a linear operator $f(a)$ on M by

$$f(a)x = [a, x],$$

then we have

$$(f(a)x, y) = -(x, f(a)y)$$

for all x and y in M, and hence, $f(a) \in L$. Since one may show that $f: M_2 \to L$ is a one-to-one Lie algebra homomorphism, it follows that

$$\dim f[M_2] = \dim M_2 = \binom{n}{2}.$$

Since the orthogonal Lie algebra L has the same dimension, $\dim L = \binom{n}{2}$, the mapping f is onto, and this establishes the isomorphism of M_2 with L.

The simply-connected Lie groups corresponding to the compact real forms of B_l and D_l are not the orthogonal groups $SO(n, \mathbb{R})$, but their covering groups Spin (n). To obtain these spin groups from the Clifford algebra, we consider the group G of all invertible elements $u \in C(M)$ such that $uzu^{-1} \in M$ for all $z \in M$. The *spin group* Spin (n) is then the identity component of the subgroup of G consisting of all elements whose left regular representation restricted to any ideal of $C(M)$ has determinant one [54], [55].

To obtain the spinor and semispinor modules, we must distinguish the case $n = 2l + 1$ with $L = B_l$ from the case $n = 2l$ with $L = D_l$. For odd n, the first Clifford algebra $C(M)$ is a semisimple associative algebra, isomorphic to the direct sum of two copies of $C^+(M)$. The second Clifford algebra $C^+(M)$ for odd n is a simple associative algebra, isomorphic to the algebra lin (N) of linear operators on some vector space N. This vector space N of dimension 2^l will turn out to be the basic spinor module over B_l. We may write $C^+(M) \approx \lin (N) \approx N \otimes N^*$, and since the basic spinor module N also happens to be self-dual, this simplifies to $C^+(M) \approx N \otimes N$. Thus, for the case n odd, the second Clifford algebra $C^+(M)$ is isomorphic, as a module over L, to the tensor square $N \otimes N$ of the basic spinor module N. For even n, the first Clifford algebra $C(M)$ itself is simple, and thus is isomorphic to the algebra of linear operators on some vector space of dimension 2^l. This vector space may be identified with the direct sum $N_1 \dotplus N_2$ of the two basic semispinor modules N_1 and N_2 over D_l, each having dimension 2^{l-1}. While the semispinor modules themselves are self-dual only for even l and each is the dual of the other for odd l, their direct sum $N_1 \dotplus N_2$ is self-dual in either case. Thus, for even n we may write the first Clifford algebra as

$$C(M) \approx \lin (N) \approx N \otimes N,$$

where $N = N_1 \dotplus N_2$. The second Clifford algebra $C^+(M)$ for even n is not simple, but only semisimple, being the direct sum of two simple ideals, namely,

$$C^+(M) \approx \lin (N_1) \dotplus \lin (N_2).$$

We shall give a detailed explanation of these constructions only for the case that n is odd. The basic spinor module N appears, roughly speaking, as the square root of the second Clifford algebra $C^+(M) \approx N \otimes N$. In order to extract this square root explicitly, it is convenient to introduce a particular basis for the fundamental module M over the orthogonal Lie algebra $L = B_l$. There is a basis $x_0, x_{\pm 1}, \cdots, x_{\pm l}$ for M such that

$$(x_i, x_j) = (x_{-i}, x_{-j}) = 0$$

and

$$(x_i, x_{-j}) = \delta_{ij}$$

for all $i, j = 1, \cdots, l$. Writing

$$\{a, b\} = ab + ba,$$

we have

$$\{x_i, x_{-j}\} = 2\delta_{ij}, \quad \cdot \ x_0^2 = 1,$$

$$\{x_i, x_j\} = \{x_{-i}, x_{-j}\} = \{x_0, x_{\pm i}\} = 0$$

for all $i, j = 1, \cdots, l$. The elements $u_i = x_0 x_i$ and $v_i = x_0 x_{-i}$, where $i = 1, \cdots, l$, generate $C^+(M)$ and satisfy

$$\{u_i, v_j\} = -2\delta_{ij}, \qquad \{u_i, u_j\} = \{v_i, v_j\} = 0.$$

A basis for $C^+(M)$ consists of the set of elements

$$u_{i_1} \cdots u_{i_r} v_{j_1} \cdots v_{j_s},$$

where $i_1 < \cdots < i_r$ and $j_1 < \cdots < j_s$. The second Clifford algebra then factorizes as a product $C^+(M) = UV$, where U and V are generated by the u's and v's respectively, together with 1. The subspace $N = U \cdot (v_1 \cdots v_l)$ $\subset C^+(M)$ is a 2^l-dimensional left ideal of $C^+(M)$. Hence $M_2 N \subset N$, and we may regard N as a module over $M_2 \approx L$.

We may illustrate this construction of the spinor module for the simplest case, corresponding to the Lie algebra $A_1 \approx B_1$. The second Clifford algebra, which in this case is the quaternion algebra, may be generated from the elements

$$u = x_0 x_{+1} = \frac{i + \sqrt{-1}j}{\sqrt{2}}$$

and

$$v = x_0 x_{-1} = \frac{i - \sqrt{-1}j}{\sqrt{2}}.$$

The algebra $C^+(M)$, spanned by $1, u, v$ and uv, factorizes as UV, where U is spanned by 1 and u, while V is spanned by 1 and v. The two-dimensional spinor module $N = Uv$ is spanned by v and uv. The factorization of the second Clifford algebra,

$$UV = C^+(M) = M_0 + M_2 \approx \mathbb{C} \dotplus L,$$

for the Lie algebra A_1 corresponds to the Clebsch–Gordan series $\{2\} \otimes \{2\}$ $\approx \{1\} \dotplus \{3\}$.

3.19 TENSOR OPERATORS

The theory of Lie groups and their representations enters in many problems in physics. We briefly discuss a few simple applications to show how Lie groups can arise and to illustrate some useful types of computational methods. The most important of these computational tools are the Clebsch–Gordan and Racah coefficients and the concept of a tensor operator.

The Clebsch–Gordan coefficients arise in connection with explicit constructions of the Clebsch–Gordan series for irreducible Lie modules. If P is an irreducible submodule included in a direct sum decomposition of $M \otimes N$, then there are certain canonical homomorphisms injecting P into $M \otimes N$ and projecting P out of $M \otimes N$. The matrix elements of these injections and projections with respect to some standard choice of module bases are called the *Clebsch–Gordan coefficients*.

The theory of irreducible tensor operators constitutes an important practical calculus for problems in atomic and nuclear physics [71], [197], [252]. Although the concept of a tensor operator was originally introduced only for the group $SU(2)$, the definition is easily generalized to the case of an arbitrary Lie algebra L. If M_1 and M_2 are modules over L, then we may regard the space $\mathrm{lin}\,(M_1, M_2)$ of all linear mappings from M_1 into M_2 as a module over L. To do so, we define the module product of an element $l \in L$ and a linear mapping $t \in \mathrm{lin}\,(M_1, M_2)$ to be the linear mapping $lt \in \mathrm{lin}\,(M_1, M_2)$ which maps any $x \in M_1$ into $(lt)x = l(tx) - t(lx) \in M_2$. We call any submodule $T \subset \mathrm{lin}\,(M_1, M_2)$ a *tensor operator module*, and its elements are called *tensor operators*. There is a natural homomorphism from $T \otimes M_1$ into M_2, and M_2 is isomorphic to a submodule of the tensor product $T \otimes M_1$. The matrix elements of the tensor operators are related to the Clebsch–Gordan coefficients which project $T \otimes M_1$ onto M_2 according to the Wigner–Eckart theorem [70], [87].

The simplest example of a tensor operator module is the trivial case for which $lt = 0$ for all $l \in L$ and all $t \in T$. In this case

$$l(tx) = t(lx)$$

for all $x \in M_1$ so that each element $t \in T$ is a module homomorphism, or as one sometimes says, a *scalar operator*. Schur's lemma can be applied to give the structure of the module homomorphisms. In particular, if M_1 and M_2 are irreducible modules, then every module homomorphism is a multiple of a given isomorphism between M_1 and M_2, if one exists, and is zero if not.

Racah coefficients typically arise in connection with recoupling problems involving tensor products of three or more Lie modules, or in computations involving tensor operators. Unlike the Clebsch–Gordan coefficients, the Racah coefficients are invariants which do not depend on the choice of module bases. For the calculation of the Racah coefficients, graphical techniques prove to be useful [3].

Lie groups sometimes arise in a physical problem because of the presence of a special dynamical symmetry. This is especially true for mathematical models which owe their solvability to the presence of such a symmetry. One interesting example is the classical Kepler problem of describing the motion of a planet about the sun, the planet being subject to a central gravitational force inversely proportional to the square of its distance from the sun. The solution of this problem leads to the familiar result that there are two possible types of motion [202]. One possibility is a periodic motion in a bounded orbit, the planet tracing out an elliptical path with the center of mass at one focal point, while the other may be described as a scattering process with a parabolic or hyperbolic trajectory. The Hamiltonian for the system is

$$H = \frac{p^2}{2m} - \frac{k}{r},$$

where p is the relative momentum, r is the distance between the sun and the planet, m is their reduced mass, and k is a constant. Due to the rotational invariance of the Hamiltonian, the angular momentum

$$\mathbf{L} = \mathbf{r} \times \mathbf{p}$$

is conserved. The three components L_x, L_y and L_z of the angular momentum form a basis for the real Lie algebra of the three-dimensional rotation group. We may recall that the Poisson bracket relations are

$$[L_i, L_j] = \varepsilon_{ijk} L_k,$$

where ε_{ijk} is the Levi–Civita tensor which is $+1$ (-1) if (i, j, k) is an even (odd) permutation of $(1, 2, 3)$ and 0 otherwise. A less obviously conserved quantity is the *Runge–Lenz vector*, defined by

$$\mathbf{A} = \frac{1}{\sqrt{2m|H|}} \left(\mathbf{L} \times \mathbf{p} + \frac{km\mathbf{r}}{r} \right).$$

It is a vector with dimensions of angular momentum pointing along the major axis of the elliptic orbit of the planet. The magnitude of the Runge–Lenz vector is equal to

$$k(m/2|H|)^{1/2}$$

times the eccentricity of the ellipse.

Some further Poisson brackets relevant to the Kepler problem may be worked out by using elementary facts from the theory of tensor operators. The method we use is taken from quantum mechanics, but it applies equally well to the classical case [74]. The analogue of the concept of a tensor operator in classical mechanics is a tensor dynamical variable, which we shall illustrate only for the case of the rotation group.

A dynamical variable S is called a *scalar dynamical variable* if its Poisson bracket with the angular momentum vanishes:

$$[\mathbf{L}, S] = 0.$$

A set of three dynamical variables $\mathbf{V} = (V_x, V_y, V_z)$ is called a *vector dynamical variable* if the Poisson bracket relations

$$[L_i, V_j] = \varepsilon_{ijk} V_k$$

hold. The dot product of two vector dynamical variables is a scalar dynamical variable, while their cross product is a vector dynamical variable. Since $\mathbf{r}$ and $\mathbf{p}$ are vector dynamical variables, it follows immediately that $\mathbf{L} \times \mathbf{p}$ is also a vector dynamical variable. Hence the Runge–Lenz vector is a vector dynamical variable, and we have

$$[L_i, A_j] = \varepsilon_{ijk} A_k.$$

The Runge–Lenz vector further satisfies

$$[A_i, A_j] = -\frac{H}{|H|} \varepsilon_{ijk} L_k.$$

For the bounded orbits, the system is invariant under a certain four-dimensional rotation group, while the symmetry group appropriate for the scattering trajectories turns out to be a Lorentz group. Since the energy is negative for the bounded orbits, we have in this case simply

$$[A_i, A_j] = \varepsilon_{ijk} L_k.$$

The vectors $\mathbf{L}$ and $\mathbf{A}$ together generate a Lie algebra which is the direct sum of two ideals, each isomorphic to $so(3, \mathbb{R})$. This algebra may be identified with

$$so(4, \mathbb{R}) \approx so(3, \mathbb{R}) \dotplus so(3, \mathbb{R}).$$

To verify this, it is convenient to introduce the quantities

$$\mathbf{J}^{\pm} = \tfrac{1}{2}(\mathbf{L} \pm \mathbf{A}).$$

These satisfy the Poisson bracket relations

$$[J_i^+, J_j^+] = \varepsilon_{ijk} J_k^+,$$

$$[J_i^-, J_j^-] = \varepsilon_{ijk} J_k^-,$$

$$[J_i^+, J_j^-] = 0.$$

Thus one of the simple ideals is generated by the elements $\mathbf{J}^+$ and the other by $\mathbf{J}^-$.

Essentially the same Kepler problem symmetry comes up again via the correspondence principle in the quantum mechanical description of the hydrogen spectrum. Here the problem is to solve the Schrödinger equation for a nonrelativistic electron moving about a proton, subject to an electro-static force satisfying an inverse-square law [254]. Formally, the Schrödinger equation is simply an eigenvalue problem for a linear operator called the Hamiltonian. The eigenvalues of the Hamiltonian operator are energy levels corresponding to the states of the system which are represented by the corresponding eigenvectors. In the hydrogen problem, one obtains a discrete spectrum, corresponding to the classical bounded orbits, and a continuous spectrum, corresponding to scattering.

An eigenvalue is called *degenerate* when the dimension of the space spanned by the corresponding eigenvectors is greater than one. In this case, more than one state corresponds to the given energy level. If the Hamiltonian does not depend explicitly on the time, the existence of conserved quantities is directly related to the degeneracy of the spectrum. In that case, the con-served dynamical variables correspond to operators which commute with the Hamiltonian. The space spanned by the eigenvectors which correspond to a given eigenvalue of the Hamiltonian is invariant under the algebra of linear operators commuting with the Hamiltonian. To put it another way, the eigenspaces corresponding to individual energy levels are modules over this *commutant algebra* [123].

For the bound states of the hydrogen atom, the commutant algebra contains a set of operators corresponding to the four-dimensional rotation group. The description of the generators $\mathbf{L}$ and $\mathbf{A}$ in the quantum mechanical problem is analogous to the discussion given for the classical problem. In quantum mechanics, however, we must replace $\mathbf{L} \times \mathbf{p}$ in the definition of the Runge–Lenz vector by

$$\tfrac{1}{2}(\mathbf{L} \times \mathbf{p} - \mathbf{p} \times \mathbf{L})$$

because these operators do not commute. The $SO(4, \mathbb{R})$ symmetry can be used to analyze the degeneracy of the spectrum of atomic hydrogen, and historically this was the way it was first done in quantum mechanics [187]. The idea is to use the two different Casimir operators, namely $\mathbf{L}^2 + \mathbf{A}^2$ and $\mathbf{A} \cdot \mathbf{L}$, of the Lie algebra $SO(4, \mathbb{R})$. The Hamiltonian H is related to the first Casimir invariant by

$$-k^2 m/2H = \mathbf{L}^2 + \mathbf{A}^2 + 1,$$

where we have chosen units in which $\hbar = 1$. From the explicit formulas for $\mathbf{L}$ and $\mathbf{A}$, it is easy to see that the other Casimir invariant $\mathbf{A} \cdot \mathbf{L}$ is always zero. Each eigenspace of the hydrogen atom Hamiltonian is a module over the Lie algebra $SO(4, \mathbb{R})$, but not all modules are actually realized as such eigenspaces.

In general, the irreducible modules over a given semisimple Lie algebra can be constructed as tensor products of irreducible modules over its simple ideals. Explicitly, if a Lie algebra L is the direct sum of two ideals $L = L_1 \oplus L_2$ and if M_1 and M_2 are irreducible modules over L_1 and L_2, respectively, then we may regard $M_1 \otimes M_2$ as an irreducible module over L.

To specify the action of L on $M_1 \otimes M_2$ it is enough to say how the Lie algebra elements act on tensor products $x_1 \otimes x_2$ of vectors $x_1 \in M_1$ and $x_2 \in M_2$. If $l = l_1 + l_2$ is the unique decomposition of an element $l \in L$ as the sum of an element $l_1 \in L_1$ and an element $l_2 \in L_2$, we set

$$l(x_1 \otimes x_2) = l_1 x_1 \otimes x_2 + x_1 \otimes l_2 x_2.$$

For the hydrogen atom, the irreducible modules can be specified by the eigenvalues of the Casimir operators $(\mathbf{J}^+)^2$ and $(\mathbf{J}^-)^2$. Since

$$(\mathbf{J}^+)^2 - (\mathbf{J}^-)^2 = \mathbf{A} \cdot \mathbf{L} = 0,$$

only those modules occur for which these eigenvalues are the same. Since

$$\mathbf{L}^2 + \mathbf{A}^2 = 2\{(\mathbf{J}^+)^2 + (\mathbf{J}^-)^2\},$$

and since

$$(\mathbf{J}^+)^2 = (\mathbf{J}^-)^2 = j(j + 1),$$

we find with $n = 2j + 1$,

$$H = -mk^2/(2n^2).$$

Thus the different irreducible modules correspond to the different energy levels of the hydrogen atom. The irreducible module corresponding to the nth energy level has dimension $(2j + 1)^2 = n^2$. The degeneracy of the nth energy level must be some multiple of n^2, and it would be n^2 if the electron had no spin. The spin of the electron contributes another factor of 2 to the degeneracy, bringing it up to $2n^2$.

The symmetry of the hydrogen atom is destroyed by any small perturbing forces, but the rotation group does not thereby lose its value. Perturbations of the Hamiltonian, such as are produced by the presence of an additional electric or magnetic field, may cause the eigenvalues to separate, so that the degeneracy disappears [167], [179]. The different states then correspond to distinct energy levels, causing what had previously been single lines of the atomic spectrum to split into several lines. Pauli used the $SO(4, \mathbb{R})$ symmetry to obtain the splitting of the hydrogen atom energy levels in a uniform magnetic field (Zeeman effect) and in a uniform electric field (Stark effect) [201]. Biedenharn has also advocated using the $SO(4, \mathbb{R})$ symmetry, which he calls the geometrization of the Coulomb field, to study the no-energy-loss Coulomb excitation of nuclear levels [31]. Biedenharn discusses the use of the Wigner–Eckart theorem to express matrix elements of tensor operators in terms of the Clebsch–Gordan coefficients for $SO(4, \mathbb{R})$.

3.20 CHARGE ALGEBRAS

The developments of the more detailed methods of representation theory have usually come from the demands of various specific applications. In particular, a good deal of activity in the area of computational representation theory has been stimulated by the needs of atomic, nuclear, and most recently, also elementary particle physics. Since one may anticipate that in the future there will also be many more areas in which these methods will find application, it is likely that this field will continue to grow for some time to come.

We discussed earlier how Lie algebras arise in the study of conservation laws in classical and quantum mechanics. The Lie algebra of all conserved quantities is usually infinite-dimensional since this algebra is closed not only under the Lie product, but also under ordinary multiplication. One can frequently obtain useful results by working with a finite-dimensional subalgebra. For example, such finite-dimensional Lie algebras often arise naturally as algebras of additive quantities. An *additive quantity* for a system of particles is a quantity which is a sum of terms, one for each particle, such that the term for a given particle depends only on the nature and coordinates of that particle. Additive quantities in physics are generally divided into two groups, those of kinematical origin, like energy and momentum, and those which are not of kinematical origin. The latter are often called *generalized charges* because the ordinary electric charge is an example of just such an object. A *conserved charge* is one which does not depend explicitly on the time and which commutes with the Hamiltonian. Besides the electric charge, there is another generalized charge which is always conserved, called the *baryon number*. Barring the existence of certain hypothetical particles called quarks, the electric charge and baryon number of every known particle in physics is an integer, positive, zero or negative.

It is widely believed that the generalized charges form a Lie algebra, and that the set of conserved charges is a subalgebra of this Lie algebra. Some evidence for this idea comes from the description of additive quantities within the formalism of quantum field theory. Here we consider only the case that all particles can be specified by means of a discrete label, which would be the case, for instance, if they were located at fixed positions and not allowed to move. One introduces for each type of particle a set of *creation* and *annihilation operators* acting on the Hilbert space of states. The creation operators $a_1^\dagger, \cdots, a_n^\dagger$ are required to be the Hermitian conjugates of the set of annihilation operators $a_1, \cdots, a_n$. If ψ is a vector in Hilbert space corresponding to some quantum state, then the vector $a_j^\dagger \psi$ corresponds to another state differing from the original state by the addition of a single particle of type j. Similarly, the vector $a_j \psi$ corresponds to a state obtained by removing a single particle of type j. These operators satisfy a certain canonical set of commutation or anticommutation relations, depending on the spin of the particle [43], [189].

For particles with integer spin, called *bosons*, they satisfy commutation relations identical to those written down for harmonic oscillators:

$$[a_i, a_j] = [a_i^\dagger, a_j^\dagger] = 0 \quad \text{and} \quad [a_i, a_j^\dagger] = \delta_{ij}.$$

One of the main reasons why the theory of harmonic oscillators is so funda-mental to quantum mechanics is just because it underlies this formal apparatus of *second quantization*. The creation and annihilation operators are to a large extent determined by their commutation relations. Formally one may regard the Hilbert space as a module over the *oscillator algebra* defined by these commutation relations. If the whole Hilbert space can be generated from a single vacuum state, for example, we obtain the *Fok representation* of this oscillator algebra [88]. Von Neumann showed that for $n < \infty$, the Fok representation is the only irreducible representation of the oscillator algebra [235]. For $n < \infty$, every representation of the oscil-lator algebra is a direct sum of Fok representations, but for $n = \infty$ the situation becomes more complicated [51].

For half-integer spin particles, called *fermions*, these creation and annihilation operators satisfy anticommutation relations,

$$\{a_i, a_j\} = \{a_i^\dagger, a_j^\dagger\} = 0 \quad \text{and} \quad \{a_i, a_j^\dagger\} = \delta_{ij},$$

where

$$\{x, y\} = xy + yx.$$

The physical significance of these relations is contained in the *Pauli exclusion principle*, according to which no two fermions can occupy the same quantum state.

The Lie algebra of all generalized charges is spanned by the elements $a_i^\dagger a_j$. One can treat the case of fermions and the case of bosons simultaneously, since in either case one can verify the commutation relations

$$[a_i^\dagger a_j, a_k^\dagger a_l] = \delta_{jk} a_i^\dagger a_l - \delta_{il} a_k^\dagger a_j.$$

Every generalized charge is an operator of the form $Q = \sum_{i,j} a_i^\dagger c_{ij} a_j$, where the c_{ij} are complex numbers. This formula, which we may rewrite as $Q = a^\dagger C a$, using an obvious matrix notation, defines a homomorphism from the Lie algebra of $n \times n$ matrices to the charge Lie algebra. If also $R = a^\dagger D a$, then from the commutation relations for $a_i^\dagger a_j$ with $a_k^\dagger a_l$ we find

$$[Q, R] = a^\dagger (CD - DC) a,$$

thus verifying that the map $C \mapsto a^\dagger C a$ is a Lie algebra homomorphism.

It would be desirable to have a more direct argument that additive quantities form a Lie algebra without appealing to the full apparatus of quantum field theory. We sketch such an argument, which is based on the notion of asymptotic products of state vectors. In order to say definitely that a system is made up of a certain number of particles, it is necessary that these particles be separated far enough apart. Otherwise their inter-actions may be strong enough to annihilate some of the particles or to create new particles. The state vector of a well-separated composite system may be described as a product of the state vectors of its component clusters [113].

In this case, the statement that A is an additive quantity may be formally interpreted as the condition

$$A(\psi\phi) = (A\psi)\phi + \psi(A\phi).$$

It is then easily seen that the commutator of two additive quantities is again an additive quantity.

Lie algebras of conserved generalized charges have recently been studied in elementary particle physics. Elementary particles engage in four distinct classes of interactions, known as the strong, electromagnetic, weak and gravitational interactions [59], [253]. The strong interactions possess greater symmetry than the others, and it is here that Lie group theory enters particle physics most directly. Not all particles engage in strong interactions; those that do are called *hadrons*, while those that do not include the leptons (neutrino, electron and muon) and their antiparticles, as well as the photon and the (hypothetical) graviton. The hadrons may be further classified by their value of the baryon number. Hadrons having baryon number 0, 1 or -1, for example, are called *mesons, baryons* and *antibaryons*, respectively. All known mesons have integer spin, while all known baryons have half-integer spin.

Because the underlying dynamics of hadrons is poorly understood, the use of symmetry considerations has been particularly valuable. Experimentally, strong interaction symmetries are manifested most strikingly in their charge and mass spectra. The earliest evidence of this sort is the near equality of the proton and neutron masses, leading to the theory of isotopic spin [119]. The state vectors for the proton and neutron span a two-dimensional module over $SU(2)$, called the *nucleon isotopic-spin doublet*. The isotopic spin operators themselves form a representation of the corresponding Lie algebra. More recently, it was found that the $SU(2)$ symmetry can be extended to an approximate $SU(3)$ symmetry [27], [100], [217]. The proton and neutron, together with the lambda Λ^0, sigma Σ^+ Σ^0 Σ^- and xi hyperons Ξ^0 Ξ^-, span an eight-dimensional module over $SU(3)$, called the *baryon octet*. The strong interactions do not preserve the $SU(3)$ symmetry, but break it in a way which allows many of the properties of hadrons to be predicted. For example, the masses of the baryons are not equal, but satisfy a simple mass formula

$$2(m_N + m_\Xi) = 3m_\Lambda + m_\Sigma$$

which can be related to the symmetry-breaking mechanism [186]. Besides the baryon octet, there are several other hadron multiplets which satisfy mass formulas consistent with $SU(3)$ symmetry. The $SU(3)$ symmetry is useful not only for the strong interaction properties of the hadrons, but also for their properties with respect to the electromagnetic and weak interactions. While these latter interactions preserve the $SU(3)$ symmetry even less than the strong interactions do, the breaking mechanisms are again very definite and many consequences can be deduced.

3.21 CLEBSCH–GORDAN COEFFICIENTS

The derivation of relations like the hadron mass formulas for $SU(3)$ involves somewhat more complicated computational techniques, especially methods for calculating Clebsch–Gordan coefficients. To illustrate these methods of representation theory, we shall work out one example for the group $SU(3)$. The interested reader should note that the computation of $SU(2)$ and $SU(3)$ Clebsch–Gordan coefficients is widely discussed in the recent literature, and both tables and computer programs are available [35], [58], [60].

The eight-dimensional representation whose Dynkin diagram is given as in Fig. 20 plays an important role in applications. The Clebsch–Gordan series

$$\{8\} \otimes \{8\} \approx \{1\} \dotplus \{8\} \dotplus \{8\} \dotplus \{10\} \dotplus \{10^*\} \dotplus \{27\}$$

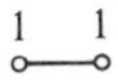

$$\overset{1\quad 1}{\circ\!\!-\!\!-\!\!\circ}\; \{8\}$$

FIG. 20. *Dynkin diagram of eight-dimensional SU(3) representation*

can be obtained either by the use of characters or by using the Young tableau technique. The two octets in the decomposition can be distinguished readily because one is symmetric and the other antisymmetric:

$$(\{8\} \otimes \{8\})_{\text{sym}} \approx \{1\} \dotplus \{8\} \dotplus \{27\},$$

$$(\{8\} \otimes \{8\})_{\text{antisym}} \approx \{8\} \dotplus \{10\} \dotplus \{10^*\}.$$

We shall work out the Clebsch–Gordan coefficients for the symmetric coupling of $\{8\} \otimes \{8\}$ to $\{8\}$. For the antisymmetric coupling one can perform a similar analysis, or one can note that the antisymmetric coupling coefficients are related directly to the structure constants of the Lie algebra. As a basis for the octet module, we can choose vectors $u_1, u_2, u_{12}, v_1, v_2,$ v_{12}, w_1 and w_2, corresponding respectively to the basis vectors $e_1, e_2, e_{12},$ f_1, f_2, f_{12}, h_1 and h_2 of the Lie algebra. The action of the Lie algebra on the octet module can be written down immediately by inspecting the commutation relations for A_2, which we wrote down earlier. For example, since $[e_1, e_2] = e_{12}$, we can immediately write

$$e_1 u_2 = u_{12} \quad \text{and} \quad e_2 u_1 = -u_{12}.$$

We list now all module products that we need:

$$
\begin{aligned}
&e_2 u_{12} = 0, &\quad &f_2 w_1 = -v_2, &\quad &e_2 u_1 = -u_{12}, \\
&e_1 u_{12} = 0, &\quad &e_2 w_1 = u_2, &\quad &e_1 w_1 = -2u_1, \\
&e_2 w_2 = -2u_2, &\quad &e_1 w_2 = u_1, &\quad &f_2 u_2 = -w_2, \\
&e_1 u_2 = u_{12}, &\quad &f_2 w_2 = -2v_2, &\quad &f_2 u_{12} = -u_1.
\end{aligned}
$$

Let us use primes to distinguish the three octet modules that are involved in our computation of the reduction

$$\{8\} \otimes \{8'\} \to \{8''\}.$$

By inspecting the weight systems, we can write down the general form for the highest weight vector of the module $\{8''\}$:

$$u''_{12} = A(u_1 \otimes u'_2 + u_2 \otimes u'_1) + B(u_{12} \otimes w'_1 + w_1 \otimes u'_{12})$$
$$+ C(u_{12} \otimes w'_2 + w_2 \otimes u'_{12}).$$

All that we have used here is the rule

$$M^\mu_H \otimes N^\nu_H \subset (M \otimes N)^{\mu+\nu}_H.$$

The coefficients A, B and C can be determined by making use of the fact that u''_{12} is an extreme vector: $e_1 u''_{12} = e_2 u''_{12} = 0$. We obtain, by a simple computation,

$$0 = e_1 u''_{12} = (A - 2B + C)(u_1 \otimes u'_{12} + u_{12} \otimes u'_1),$$
$$0 = e_2 u''_{12} = (-A + B - 2C)(u_2 \otimes u'_{12} + u_{12} \otimes u'_2),$$

and thus,

$$A - 2B + C = 0, \qquad -A + B - 2C = 0.$$

The overall normalization is left undetermined, since we have not specified any particular normalization for our basis, and we might as well choose $B = 1$, say, so that we obtain

$$A = 3, \quad B = 1, \quad C = -1.$$

Thus we obtain, for the highest weight vector,

$$u''_{12} = 3(u_1 \otimes u'_2 + u_2 \otimes u'_1)$$
$$+ u_{12} \otimes (w'_1 - w'_2) + (w_1 - w_2) \otimes u'_{12}.$$

The remaining basis vectors of the module $\{8''\}$ can be obtained by applying the lowering algebra to this highest weight vector. For example, the equation $[f_2, e_{12}] = -e_1$ allows us to write down

$$u''_1 = -f_2 u''_{12}.$$

Using our formula for u''_{12}, we then can immediately calculate u''_1, obtaining

$$u''_1 = 3(u_{12} \otimes v'_2 + v_2 \otimes u'_{12}) + u_1 \otimes (w'_1 + 2w'_2) + (w_1 + 2w_2) \otimes u'_1.$$

An interesting feature of our computation of Clebsch–Gordan coefficients in this example is that only integers appear. The reason that it is possible for us to obtain integer Clebsch–Gordan coefficients is essentially that we have not used the normalization conventions which are customarily imposed [72]. Being able to work just with integers is extremely useful for programming automatic electronic digital computers to compute Clebsch–Gordan coefficients. A general proof that it is always possible to choose module bases for which the Clebsch–Gordan coefficients are integers for any simple Lie algebra has been given recently by Chevalley [57], [212].

It should be noted that in the course of solving the equations which determine the extreme subspace in a given reduction, it sometimes happens that we obtain more than one extreme vector with the same weight. This is sometimes referred to as the *multiplicity problem* for Clebsch–Gordan coefficients. In the preceding discussion, for example, there are two octet submodules in the tensor product $\{8\} \otimes \{8\}$, which we could distinguish on the basis of symmetry. But even if there were no symmetry to distinguish such isomorphic submodules, we could still find a basis for the extreme subspace. Finding such a basis using integer mode arithmetic amounts to solving a set of Diophantine linear equations, as our example shows. The solution of such a set of equations is equivalent to finding a basis for a finitely generated Abelian group. This can be done automatically on a computer by the use of an algorithm published recently by D. A. Smith [213], [220]. Therefore, at least in principle, all multiplicity problems can be resolved in the calculation of Clebsch–Gordan coefficients for any simple Lie algebra.

In practice, however, this method is seldom used by physicists because they are usually interested in unitary representations. For the unitary representations, it is often more useful to employ an orthonormal basis, even though this means giving up integer Clebsch–Gordan coefficients. Although there is no uniform method for finding such orthonormal bases which applies to any simple Lie algebra, much work has been done for various special cases. In the case of $SU(n)$, for example, much work has been done to calculate Clebsch–Gordan coefficients using a basis discovered by Gelfand and Zetlin [153].

BIBLIOGRAPHY

[1] R. ABRAHAM, *Foundations of Mechanics. A Mathematical Exposition of Classical Mechanics with an Introduction to the Qualitative Theory of Dynamical Systems and Applications to the Three-Body Problem*, Mathematical Physics Monograph Series, W. A. Benjamin, New York, 1967.

[2] I. D. ADO, *The representation of Lie algebras by matrices*, Uspekhi Mat. Nauk (22) 3 (1947), no. 6, pp. 159–173; English transl., Amer. Math. Soc. Transl. no. 2, 1949.

[3] V. K. AGRAWALA AND J. G. F. BELINFANTE, *Graphical formulation of recoupling theory for any compact group*, Ann. Physics, 49 (1968), pp. 130–170.

[4] ——, *Weight diagrams for Lie group representations: A computer implementation of Freudenthal's algorithm in ALGOL and FORTRAN*, BIT, 9 (1969), pp. 301–314.

[5] ——, *An algorithm for computing SU(n) invariants*, BIT, 11 (1971), pp. 1–15.

[6] C. M. ANDERSEN, *Clebsch–Gordan series for symmetrized tensor products*, J. Mathematical Phys., 8 (1967), pp. 988–997.

[7] J. P. ANTOINE, *Irreducible representations of the group SU(3)*, Ann. Soc. Sci. Bruxelles Sér. I., 77 (1963), pp. 150–162.

[8] J. P. ANTOINE AND D. R. SPEISER, *Characters of the irreducible representations of the simple groups. I*, J. Mathematical Phys., 5 (1964), pp. 1226–1234.

[9] ——, *Characters of the irreducible representations of the simple groups. II: Application to classical groups*, Ibid., 5 (1964), pp. 1560–1572.

[10] E. ARTIN, *Geometric Algebra*, Interscience Tracts in Pure and Applied Mathematics, vol. 3, Interscience, New York, 1957.

[11] E. W. ASLAKSEN AND J. R. KLAUDER, *Unitary representations of the affine group*, J. Mathematical Phys., 9 (1968), pp. 206–211.

[12] ——, *Continuous representation theory using the affine group*, Ibid., 10 (1969), pp. 2267–2275.

[13] H. BACRY, *Position and polarization operators in relativistic and nonrelativistic mechanics*, Ibid., 5 (1964), pp. 109–111.

[14] G. E. BAIRD AND L. C. BIEDENHARN, JR., *On the representation of the semisimple Lie groups. II*, Ibid., 4 (1963), pp. 1449–1466.

[15] G. A. BAKER, *Degeneracy of the n-dimensional isotropic harmonic oscillator*, Phys. Rev., 103 (1956), pp. 1119–1120.

[16] H. F. BAKER, *Alternants and continuous groups*, Proc. London Math. Soc. (2), 3 (1904), pp. 24–47.

[17] V. BARGMANN, *Irreducible unitary representations of the Lorentz group*, Ann. of Math. (2), 48 (1947), pp. 568–642.

[18] ——, *On unitary ray representations of continuous groups*, Ibid., (2), 59 (1954), pp. 1–46.

[19] ——, *Note on Wigner's theorem on symmetry operations*, J. Mathematical Phys., 5 (1964), pp. 862–868.

[20] V. BARGMANN AND M. MOSHINSKY, *Group theory of harmonic oscillators. Part I: The collective modes*, Nuclear Phys., 18 (1960), pp. 697–712.

[21] D. W. BARNES, *Nilpotency of Lie algebras*, Math. Z., 79 (1962), pp. 237–238.

149

[22] D. W. BARNES, *Lattice isomorphisms of Lie algebras*, J. Australian Math. Soc., 4 (1964), pp. 470–475.

[23] ———, *On Cartan subalgebras of Lie algebras*, Math. Z., 101 (1967), pp. 350–355; Erratum, Math. Z., 111 (1969), p. 168.

[24] R. E. BECK AND B. KOLMAN, *Generation of the Weyl group on a computer*, J. Computational Phys., 7 (1971), pp. 346–353.

[25] ———, *Computer approaches to the representations of Lie algebras*, J. Assoc. Comput. Mach., to appear.

[26] ———, *A computer implementation of Freudenthal's multiplicity formula*, to be published.

[27] R. E. BEHRENDS, J. DREITLEIN, C. FRONSDAL AND B. W. LEE, *Simple groups and strong interaction symmetries*, Rev. Modern Phys., 34 (1962), pp. 1–40.

[28] J. G. F. BELINFANTE, B. KOLMAN AND H. A. SMITH, *An introduction to Lie groups and Lie algebras, with applications*, SIAM Rev., 8 (1966), pp. 11–46.

[29] ———, *An introduction to Lie groups and Lie algebras, with applications. II: The basic methods and results of representation theory*, Ibid., 10 (1968), pp. 160–195.

[30] J. G. F. BELINFANTE AND B. KOLMAN, *An introduction to Lie groups and Lie algebras, with applications. III: Computational methods and applications of representation theory*, Ibid., 11 (1969), pp. 510–543.

[31] L. C. BIEDENHARN, JR., *Wigner coefficients for the R_4 group and some applications*, J. Mathematical Phys., 2 (1961), pp. 433–441.

[32] L. C. BIEDENHARN, JR. AND W. J. HOLMAN, III, *Complex angular momenta and the groups $SU(1, 1)$ and $SU(2)$*, Ann. Physics, 39 (1966), pp. 1–42.

[33] G. BIRKHOFF, *Lie groups isomorphic with no linear group*, Bull. Amer. Math. Soc., 42 (1936), pp. 882–888.

[34] ———, *Hydrodynamics: A Study in Logic, Fact, and Similitude*, Princeton Univ. Press, Princeton, N.J., 1950.

[35] R. BIVINS, N. METROPOLIS, M. ROTENBERG AND J. K. WOOTEN, JR., *The $3 - j$ and $6 - j$ Symbols*, The M.I.T. Press, Cambridge, Mass., 1959.

[36] A. BOREL, *Topology of Lie groups and characteristic classes*, Bull. Amer. Math. Soc., 61 (1955), pp. 397–432.

[37] R. BRANTON, *A generalization of the fundamental theorem of projective geometry*, Doctoral thesis, University of Pennsylvania, Philadelphia, 1970.

[38] F. BRICKELL AND R. S. CLARK, *Differentiable Manifolds: An Introduction*, Van Nostrand-Reinhold, London, 1970.

[39] H. C. BRINKMAN, *Applications of Spinor Invariants in Atomic Physics*, North Holland, Amsterdam, 1956.

[40] R. BROCKETT, *System theory on group manifolds and coset spaces*, SIAM J. Control, 10 (1972), pp. 265–284.

[41] G. BROWN, *A remark on semisimple Lie algebras*, Proc. Amer. Math. Soc., 15 (1964), p. 518.

[42] F. BRUHAT, *Lectures on Lie groups and representations of locally compact groups*, Lecture notes, Tata Institute of Fundamental Research, Bombay, India, 1958.

[43] N. BURGOYNE, *On the connection of spin with statistics*, Nuovo Cimento, 8 (1958), pp. 607–609.

[44] J. E. CAMPBELL, *On a law of combination of operators*, Proc. London Math. Soc., 29 (1898), pp. 14–32.

[45] É. CARTAN, *Projective groups which do not leave any flat manifold invariant*, Bull. Soc. Math. France, 41 (1913), pp. 53–96 (in French).

[46] ———, *The finite and continuous real simple groups*, Ann. Sci. École Norm. Sup., 31 (1914), pp. 263–355 (in French).

[47] P. CARTIER, *Finite groups generated by reflections*, Seminaire Chevalley, vol. 2, exposé 14, École Normale Supérieure, Paris, 1957/1958 (in French).

[48] ———, *On H. Weyl's character formula*, Bull. Amer. Math. Soc., 67 (1961), pp. 228–230.

[49] H. CASIMIR, *On the construction of a differential equation corresponding to the irreducible representations of semisimple continuous groups*, Proc. Konikl. Akad. Amsterdam, 34 (1931), pp. 844–846 (in German).

[50] H. CASIMIR AND B. L. VAN DER WAERDEN, *Algebraic proof of the complete reducibility of the representations of semisimple groups*, Math. Ann., 111 (1935), pp. 1–12 (in German).

[51] J. M. CHAIKEN, *Number operators for representations of the canonical commutation relations*, Comm. Math. Phys., 8 (1968), pp. 164–184.

[52] K. T. CHEN, *Formal differential equations*, Ann. of Math. (2), 73 (1961), pp. 110–133.

[53] ———, *Decomposition of differential equations*, Math. Ann., 146 (1962), pp. 263–278.

[54] C. C. CHEVALLEY, *Theory of Lie Groups*, vol. I, Princeton Univ. Press, Princeton, N.J., 1946.

[55] ———, *The Algebraic Theory of Spinors*, Columbia Univ. Press, New York, 1954.

[56] ———, *The Construction and Study of Certain Important Algebras*, Mathematical Society of Japan, Tokyo, 1955.

[57] ———, *On Certain Simple Groups*, Tôhoku Math. J. (2), 7 (1955), pp. 14–66 (in French).

[58] C.-K. CHEW AND H. C. VON BAEYER, *Explicit computation of the SU(3) Clebsch–Gordan coefficients*, Nuovo Cimento, 56 A (1968), pp. 53–63.

[59] G. F. CHEW, M. GELL-MANN AND A. H. ROSENFELD, *Strongly interacting particles*, Scientific American, 210 (1964), no. 2, pp. 74–93.

[60] F. CHILTON AND P. McNAMEE, *Tables of Clebsch–Gordan coefficients of SU(3)*, Rev. Modern Phys., 36 (1964), pp. 1005–1024.

[61] Y. CHOW, *Gel'fand–Kirillov conjecture on the Lie field of an algebraic Lie algebra*, J. Mathematical Phys. 10 (1969), pp. 975–992.

[62] W. K. CLIFFORD, *Applications of Grassman's extensive algebra*, Amer. J. Math., 1 (1878), pp. 350–358.

[63] A. COHEN, *An Introduction to the Lie Theory of One-Parameter Groups*, Stechert, New York, 1931.

[64] P. M. COHN, *Lie Groups*, Cambridge Tracts in Mathematics and Mathematical Physics, No. 46, Cambridge Univ. Press, Cambridge, 1957.

[65] H. C. CORBEN AND P. STEHLE, *Classical Mechanics*, 2nd ed., John Wiley, New York, 1960.

[66] E. M. CORSON, *Introduction to Tensors, Spinors and Relativistic Wave Equations*, Blackie & Son, London, 1953.

[67] H. S. M. COXETER, *Discrete groups generated by reflections*, Ann. of Math. (2), 35 (1934), pp. 588–621.

[68] ———, *The product of the generators of a finite group generated by reflections*, Duke Math. J., 18 (1951), pp. 765–782.

[69] H. S. M. COXETER AND W. O. J. MOSER, *Generators and Relations for Discrete Groups*, Springer-Verlag, Berlin, 1957.

[70] J. R. DEROME AND W. T. SHARP, *Racah algebra for an arbitrary group*, J. Mathematical Phys., 6 (1965), pp. 1584–1590.

[71] A. DE SHALIT AND I. TALMI, *Nuclear Shell Theory*, Academic Press, New York, 1963.

[72] J. J. DE SWART, *The octet model and its Clebsch–Gordan coefficients*, Rev. Modern Phys., 35 (1963), pp. 916–939; Erratum: Rev. Modern Phys., 37 (1965), p. 326.

[73] H. DE VRIES AND H. FREUDENTHAL, *Linear Lie Groups*, Academic Press, New York, 1969.

[74] R. H. DICKE AND J. P. WITTKE, *Introduction to Quantum Mechanics*, Addison-Wesley, Reading, Mass., 1960.

[75] P. A. M. DIRAC, *Relativity quantum mechanics with application to Compton scattering*, Proc. Roy. Soc. London, A 111 (1926), pp. 405–423.

[76] ———, *On the analogy between classical and quantum mechanics*, Rev. Modern Phys., 17 (1945), pp. 195–199.

[77] P. A. M. DIRAC, *Generalized Hamiltonian dynamics*, Canad. J. Math., 2 (1950), pp. 129–148.

[78] ——, *Generalized Hamiltonian dynamics*, Proc. Roy. Soc. London, A 246 (1958), pp. 326–332.

[79] ——, *Principles of Quantum Mechanics*, 4th ed., Clarendon Press, Oxford, 1958.

[80] N. DUNFORD AND J. T. SCHWARTZ, *Linear Operators, Part II. Spectral Theory: Self-Adjoint Operators in Hilbert Space*, Interscience, New York, 1963.

[81] E. B. DYNKIN, *The structure of semisimple algebras*, Uspekhi Mat. Nauk, 2 (1947), pp. 59–127; English transl., Amer. Math. Soc. Transl. No. 17, 1950, reprinted in Amer. Math. Soc. Translations Series I, vol. 9, 1962, pp. 328–469.

[82] ——, *Semisimple subalgebras of semisimple Lie algebras*, Mat. Sb., 30 (1952), pp. 349–462; English transl., Amer. Math. Soc. Translations Series II, vol. 6, 1957, pp. 111–244.

[83] ——, *The maximal subgroups of the classical groups*, Trudy Moskov. Mat. Obshch., 1 (1952), pp. 39–166, includes supplement, *Survey of the basic concepts and facts in the theory of linear representations of semisimple Lie algebras*; English transl., Amer. Math. Soc. Transl. (2), 6 (1957), pp. 245–378.

[84] A. R. EDMONDS, *Angular Momentum in Quantum Mechanics*, Princeton Univ. Press, Princeton, N.J., 1957.

[85] D. L. ELLIOTT, *A consequence of controllability*, J. Differential Equations, 10 (1971), pp. 364–370.

[86] D. L. ELLIOTT AND D. J. TARN, *Controllability and observability for bilinear systems*, preprint, (1971).

[87] U. FANO AND G. RACAH, *Irreducible Tensorial Sets*, Academic Press, New York, 1959.

[88] V. FOCK, *Configuration space and Dirac's method of quantization*, Z. Physik, 75 (1932), pp. 622–647.

[89] H. FREUDENTHAL, *On the calculation of the characters of semisimple Lie groups. I*, Nederl. Akad. Wetensch. Proc. Ser. A, A 57(1954), pp. 369–376; Nederl. Akad. Wetensch. Indag. Math., 16 (1954), pp. 369–376 (both in German).

[90] ——, *On the calculation of the characters of semisimple Lie groups. II*, Nederl. Akad. Wetensch. Proc. Ser. A, A 57(1954), pp. 487–491; Nederl. Akad. Wetensch. Indag. Math., 16 (1954), pp. 487–491 (both in German).

[91] ——, *On the calculation of the characters of semisimple Lie groups. III*, Nederl. Akad. Wetensch. Proc. Ser. A, A 59 (1956), pp. 511–514; Nederl. Akad. Wetensch. Indag. Math., 18 (1956), pp. 511–514 (both in German).

[92] ——, *Lie Groups*, Yale University Lecture Notes, New Haven, Connecticut, 1961, unpublished.

[93] F. GANTMACHER, *Canonical representations of automorphisms of a complex semisimple Lie Group*, Mat. Sb., 5 (1939), pp. 101–146 (in English).

[94] ——, *On the classification of real simple Lie groups*, Ibid., 5 (1939), pp. 217–249.

[95] L. GÅRDING, *Relativistic wave equations for zero rest-mass*, Proc. Cambridge Philos. Soc., 41 (1945), pp. 49–56.

[96] ——, *Note on continuous representations of Lie groups*, Proc. Nat. Acad. Sci. U.S.A., 33 (1947), pp. 331–332.

[97] L. GÅRDING AND A. S. WIGHTMAN, *Representations of the commutation relations*, Ibid., 40 (1954), pp. 622–626.

[98] I. M. GEL'FAND AND A. A. KIRILLOV, *Fields associated with enveloping algebras of Lie algebras*, Dokl. Akad. Nauk SSSR, 167 (1966), pp. 503–505; English transl., Soviet Math. Dokl., 7 (1966), pp. 407–409.

[99] ——, *The structure of the quotient field of the enveloping algebra of a semisimple Lie algebra*, Dokl. Akad. Nauk SSSR, 180 (1968), pp. 775–777; English transl., Soviet Math. Dokl., 9 (1968), pp. 669–671.

[100] M. GELL-MANN AND Y. NE'EMAN, *The Eightfold Way*, W. A. Benjamin, New York, 1964.

[101] R. C. GLAESER AND B. KOLMAN, *Lattice isomorphisms of solvable Lie algebras*, J. Australian Math. Soc., 10 (1969), pp. 266–268.

[102] R. GODEMENT, *A theory of spherical functions. I*, Trans. Amer. Math. Soc., 73 (1952), pp. 496–555.

[103] R. H. GOOD, *Properties of the Dirac matrices*, Rev. Modern Phys., 27 (1955), pp. 187–211.

[104] M. GOTÔ, *On algebraic Lie algebras*, J. Math. Soc. Japan, 1 (1948), pp. 29–45.

[105] ———, *Lattices of subalgebras of real Lie algebras*, J. Algebra, 11 (1969), pp. 6–24.

[106] M. GOURDIN, *Unitary Symmetries and Their Application to High-Energy Physics*, North Holland, Amsterdam, 1967.

[107] S. GREENSPAN AND R. D. RICHTMYER, *Expansion of the Campbell-Baker-Hausdorff formula by computer*, Comm. Pure Appl. Math., 18 (1965), pp. 107–108.

[108] H. J. GROENEWOLD, *On the principles of elementary quantum mechanics*, Physica, 12 (1946), pp. 405–474.

[109] B. GRUBER, *Lecture notes on multiplicities in the classical groups*, Instituto di Fisica Teorica, Universita di Napoli, Naples, Italy, 1968, unpublished.

[110] ———, *Recurrence relations for the multiplicities in the classical groups*, J. Mathematical Phys., 11 (1970), pp. 1783–1790.

[111] B. GRUBER AND H. J. WEBER, *On the construction of weight diagrams for SO(5), Sp(4) and G_2*, Proc. Roy. Irish Acad. Sect. A, 66 A (1968), pp. 31–40.

[112] K. W. GRUENBERG AND A. J. WEIR, *Linear Geometry*, Van Nostrand, Princeton, N.J., 1967.

[113] R. HAAG, *The framework of quantum field theory*, Nuovo Cimento Suppl., 14 (1959), pp. 131–152.

[114] P. R. HALMOS, *Finite-Dimensional Vector Spaces*, 2nd ed., Van Nostrand, Princeton, N.J., 1958.

[115] M. HAMERMESH, *Group Theory and its Applications to Physical Problems*, Addison-Wesley, Reading, Mass., 1962.

[116] HARISH-CHANDRA, *On representations of Lie algebras*, Ann. of Math. (2), 50 (1949), pp. 900–915.

[117] ———, *On the radical of a Lie algebra*, Proc. Amer. Math. Soc., 1 (1950), pp. 14–17.

[118] F. HAUSDORFF, *The symbolic exponential formula in group theory*, Ber. Verh. Sächs. Ges. Wiss. Leipzig. Math.-Phys. Kl., 58 (1906), pp. 19–48 (in German).

[119] W. HEISENBERG, *On the structure of the atomic nucleus. I*, Z. Physik, 77 (1932), pp. 1–11 (in German).

[120] S. HELGASON, *Differential Geometry and Symmetric Spaces*, Academic Press, New York, 1962.

[121] K. HELMERS, *Symplectic invariants and Flowers' classification of shell model states*, Nuclear Phys., 23 (1961), pp. 594–611.

[122] J. C. HERZ, *Contribution to the algebraic theory of partial differential equations*, Ann. Sci. École Norm. Sup., 71 (1954), pp. 321–362.

[123] E. L. HILL AND J. M. JAUCH, *On the problem of degeneracy in quantum mechanics*, Phys. Rev., 57 (1940), pp. 641–645.

[124] G. HOCHSCHILD, *The Structure of Lie Groups*, Holden-Day, San Francisco, 1965.

[125] W. C. HOFFMAN, *The neuron as a Lie group germ and a Lie product*, Quart. Appl. Math., 25 (1968), pp. 423–440.

[126] H. HOPF, *Vector fields in n-dimensional manifolds*, Math. Ann., 96 (1926), pp. 225–250 (in German).

[127] H. HOPF AND W. RINOW, *On the concept of a complete differential-geometric surface*, Comment. Math. Helv., 3 (1931), pp. 209–225 (in German).

[128] T. E. HULL AND L. INFIELD, *The factorization method*, Rev. Modern Phys., 23 (1951), pp. 21–68.

[129] T. HUSAIN, *Introduction to Topological Groups*, W. B. Saunders, Philadelphia, 1966.

[130] E. L. INCE, *Ordinary Differential Equations*, Longmans, Green & Co., London, 1926; reprinted by Dover Publications, New York, 1956.

[131] C. ITZYKSON AND M. NAUENBERG, *Unitary groups: Representations and decompositions*, Rev. Modern Phys., 38 (1966), pp. 95–120.

[132] M. JACOB AND G. C. WICK, *On the general theory of collisions for particles with spin*, Ann. Physics, 7 (1959), pp. 404–428.

[133] N. JACOBSON, *Rational methods in the theory of Lie algebras*, Ann. of Math. (2), 36 (1935), pp. 875–881.

[134] ———, *Lectures in Abstract Algebra. Volume II: Linear Algebra*, Van Nostrand, Princeton, N.J., 1953.

[135] ———, *Lie Algebras*, Interscience Tracts in Pure and Applied Mathematics, No. 10, Interscience, New York, 1962.

[136] ———, *Lectures in Abstract Algebra. Volume III: Theory of Fields and Galois Theory*, Van Nostrand, Princeton, N.J., 1964.

[137] A. JOSEPH, *Derivations of Lie brackets and canonical quantization*, Comm. Math. Phys., 17 (1970), pp. 210–232.

[138] R. JOST, *Poisson brackets (an unpedagogical lecture)*, Rev. Modern Phys., 36 (1964), pp. 572–579.

[139] R. E. KALMAN, *Mathematical description of linear dynamical systems*, SIAM J. Control, 1 (1963), pp. 152–192.

[140] A. U. KLIMYK, *Multiplicities of weights of representations and multiplicities of representations of semisimple Lie algebras*, Soviet Math. Dokl., 8 (1967), pp. 1531–1534.

[141] B. KOLMAN, *Semi-modular Lie algebras*, J. Sci. Hiroshima University Ser. A–I Math., 29 (1965), pp. 149–163.

[142] ———, *Relatively complemented Lie algebras*, Ibid., 31 (1967), pp. 1–11.

[143] M. KONUMA, K. SHIMA AND M. WADA, *Simple Lie algebras of rank 3 and symmetries of elementary particles in the strong interactions*, Progr. Theoret. Phys. (Japan) Suppl., 28 (1963), pp. 1–128.

[144] P. KOOSIS, *An irreducible unitary representation of a compact group is finite-dimensional*, Proc. Amer. Math. Soc., 8 (1957), pp. 712–715.

[145] B. KOSTANT, *A formula for the multiplicity of a weight*, Proc. Nat. Acad. Sci. U.S.A., 44 (1958), pp. 588–589.

[146] ———, *A formula for the multiplicity of a weight*, Trans. Amer. Math. Soc., 93 (1959), pp. 53–73.

[147] ———, *Lie group representations on polynomial rings*, Bull. Amer. Math. Soc., 69 (1963), pp. 518–526.

[148] M. I. KRUSEMEYER, *Determining multiplicities of dominant weights in irreducible Lie algebra representations using a computer*, BIT, 11 (1971), pp. 310–316.

[149] J. KUCERA, *Solution in large of control problem* $\dot{x} = (A(1 - v) + Bv)x$, Czechoslovak. Math. J., 16 (1966), no. 91, pp. 600–623.

[150] ———, *Solution in large of control problem* $\dot{x} = (Au + Bv)x$, Ibid., 17 (1967), no. 92, pp. 91–96.

[151] E. E. LEVI, *On the structure of finite and continuous groups*, Atti Accad. Torino, 40 (1905), pp. 3–17 (in Italian).

[152] L. H. LOOMIS, *An Introduction to Abstract Harmonic Analysis*, Van Nostrand, New York, 1953.

[153] J. D. LOUCK, *Recent progress toward a theory of tensor operators in the unitary groups*, Amer. J. Phys., 38 (1970), pp. 3–42.

[154] G. LOUPIAS, M. SIRUGUE AND J. C. TROTIN, *On simple Lie groups of rank 3*, Nuovo Cimento. 38 (1965), pp. 1303–1325.

[155] A. J. MACFARLANE, L. O'RAIFEARTAIGH AND P. S. RAO, *Relationship of the internal and external multiplicity structure of compact simple Lie groups*, J. Mathematical Phys., 8 (1967), pp. 536–546.

[156] G. W. MACKEY, *Infinite-dimensional group representations*, Bull. Amer. Math. Soc., 69 (1963), pp. 628–686.

[157] S. MacLANE, *Natural associativity and commutativity*, Rice Univ. Studies, 49 (1963), pp. 28–46.

[158] P. A. MacMAHON, *Combinatory Analysis*, vol. II, Cambridge University Press, Cambridge, 1916.

[159] W. MAGNUS, *On the exponential solution of differential equations for a linear operator*, Comm. Pure Appl. Math., 7 (1954), pp. 649–673.

[160] A. I. MAL'CEV, *On the representation of an algebra as a direct sum of its radical and a semi-simple subalgebra*, Dokl. Akad. Nauk SSSR, 36 (1942), pp. 42–45.

[161] ———, *On semisimple subgroups of Lie groups*, Amer. Math. Soc. Transl. (I), 9 (1962), pp. 172–213.

[162] K. MAURIN, *General Eigenfunction Expansions and Unitary Representations of Topological Groups*, Polish Scientific Publishers, Warsaw, Poland, 1968.

[163] W. MAYER AND T. Y. THOMAS, *Foundations of the theory of Lie groups*, Ann. of Math. (2), 36 (1935), pp. 770–822.

[164] G. McCARTY, *Topology: An Introduction with Application to Topological Groups*, McGraw-Hill, New York, 1967.

[165] J. McCONNELL, *Multiplicities in weight diagrams*, Proc. Roy. Irish Acad. Sect. A, A 65 (1966), pp. 1–12.

[166] ———, *Properties of the exceptional G_2 Lie group*, Ibid., A 66 (1968), pp. 72–92.

[167] A. MESSIAH, *Quantum Mechanics*, vol. II, North Holland, Amsterdam, 1962.

[168] W. MILLER, JR., *On Lie algebras and some special functions of mathematical physics*, Mem. Amer. Math. Soc., no. 50, 1964.

[169] ———, *Lie Theory and Special Functions*, Math. Sci. Engrg. Series, vol. 43, Academic Press, New York, 1968.

[170] D. MONTGOMERY AND L. ZIPPIN, *Topological Transformation Groups*, Interscience, New York, 1955.

[171] C. B. MORREY, *The analytic embedding of abstract real-analytic manifolds*, Ann. of Math. (2), 68 (1958), pp. 159–201.

[172] H. E. MOSES, *Reduction of reducible representations of the Poincaré group to standard helicity representations*, J. Mathematical Phys., 9 (1968), pp. 2039–2049.

[173] M. MOSHINSKY, *The harmonic oscillator and supermultiplet theory. I: The single shell picture*, Nuclear Phys., 31 (1962), pp. 384–405.

[174] G. M. MUBARAKZJANOV, *On solvable Lie algebras*, Izv. Vyssh. Uchebn. Zaved. Matematika, 1 (1963), no. 32, pp. 114–123 (in Russian).

[175] ———, *Classification of real structures of Lie algebras of fifth order*, Ibid., 3 (1963), no. 34, pp. 99–106 (in Russian).

[176] ———, *Classification of solvable Lie algebras of sixth order with a non-nilpotent basis element*, Ibid., 4 (1963), no. 35, pp. 104–116 (in Russian).

[177] ———, *Certain theorems on solvable Lie algebras*, Ibid., 6 (1966), no. 55, pp. 95–98 (in Russian).

[178] S. MURAKAMI, *On the classification of real simple Lie algebras*, Osaka J. Math., 2 (1965), pp. 291–307 (in French).

[179] F. J. MURRAY, *Perturbation theory and Lie algebras*, J. Mathematical Phys., 3 (1962), pp. 451–468.

[180] L. NACHBIN, *On the finite dimensionality of every irreducible representation of a compact group*, Proc. Amer. Math. Soc., 12 (1961), pp. 11–12.

[181] M. A. NAĬMARK, *Normed Rings*, P. Noordhoff, Groningen, the Netherlands, 1964.

[182] ———, *Linear Representations of the Lorentz Group*, Fizmatgiz, Moscow, 1958 (in Russian); English transl., Macmillan, New York, 1964.

[183] Y. NE'EMAN, *The symmetry approach to particle physics*, Proc. International Conference on Nuclear Structure, 1963, pp. 172–187; Reprinted in Gell-Mann and Ne'eman, *The Eightfold Way*, W. A. Benjamin, New York, 1964, pp. 302–317.

[184] E. NORMAN AND J. WEI, *Lie algebraic solution of linear differential equations*, J. Mathematical Phys., 4 (1963), pp. 575–581.

[185] ——, *On global representations of the solutions of linear differential equations as a product of exponentials*, Proc. Amer. Math. Soc., 15 (1964), pp. 327–334.

[186] S. OKUBO, *Note on unitary symmetry in strong interactions*, Prog. Theoret. Phys., 27 (1962), pp. 949–966.

[187] W. PAULI, JR., *On the hydrogen spectrum from the standpoint of the new quantum mechanics*, Z. Physik, 36 (1926), pp. 336–363.

[188] ——, *Mathematical contributions to the theory of Dirac matrices*, Ann. Inst. H. Poincaré, 6 (1936), pp. 109–136 (in French).

[189] ——, *The connection between spin and statistics*, Phys. Rev., 58 (1940), pp. 716–722.

[190] ——, *Continuous groups in quantum mechanics*, Ergeb. d. Exakt. Naturw., vol. 37, G. Höhler, ed., Springer-Verlag, Berlin, 1965, pp. 85–104 (Posthumous publication of 1958 CERN Report).

[191] S. PERLIS, *Theory of Matrices*, Addison-Wesley, Cambridge, Mass., 1952.

[192] L. S. PONTRYAGIN, *Topological Groups*, 2nd ed., Gordon and Breach, New York, 1966.

[193] L. PUKÁNSZKY, *On the Kronecker products of irreducible representations of the 2×2 real unimodular group. I*, Trans. Amer. Math. Soc., 100 (1961), pp. 116–152.

[194] G. RACAH, *Theory of complex spectra. IV*, Phys. Rev., 76 (1949), pp. 1352–1365.

[195] ——, *On the decomposition of tensors by contraction*, Rev. Modern Phys., 21 (1949), pp. 494–496.

[196] ——, *Lectures on Lie groups*, Group Theoretical Concepts and Methods in Elementary Particle Physics, F. Gürsey, ed., Gordon and Breach, New York, 1964, pp. 1–36.

[197] ——, *Group theory and spectroscopy*, Ergeb. d. Exakt. Naturw., vol. 37, G. Höhler, ed., Springer-Verlag, Tracts in Modern Physics, Berlin, 1965, pp. 28–84 (Reprint of 1951 lecture notes).

[198] D. RADHAKRISHNAN, *On the Clebsch–Gordan series of a semisimple Lie algebra*, J. Mathematical Phys., 9 (1968), pp. 2061–2063.

[199] D. RADHAKRISHNAN AND T. S. SANTHANAM, *Internal multiplicity structure and Clebsch–Gordan series for the exceptional group G(2)*, Ibid., 8 (1967), pp. 2206–2209.

[200] S. RAMANUJAM, *Topology of classical groups*, Osaka J. Math., 6 (1969), pp. 243–249.

[201] P. J. REDMOND, *Generalization of the Runge–Lenz vector in the presence of an electric field*, Phys. Rev., 133 (1964), pp. 1352–1353.

[202] D. E. RICHMOND, *Inverse square orbits: A simple treatment*, Amer. Math. Monthly, 59 (1952), pp. 694–696.

[203] M. E. ROSE, *Elementary Theory of Angular Momentum*, John Wiley, New York, 1957.

[204] D. E. RUTHERFORD, *Substitutional Analysis*, Edinburgh University Press, Edinburgh, 1948.

[205] H. SAMELSON, *Topology of Lie groups*, Bull. Amer. Math. Soc., 58 (1952), pp. 2–37.

[206] T. SATAKE, *On representations and compactifications of symmetric spaces*, Ann. of Math. (2), 71 (1960), pp. 77–110.

[207] R. D. SCHAFER, *An Introduction to Nonassociative Algebras*, Academic Press, New York, 1966.

[208] J. A. SCHOUTEN, *Tensor Analysis for Physicists*, Clarendon Press, Oxford, 1954.

[209] J. P. SERRE, *Semisimple Complex Lie Algebras*, W. A. Benjamin, New York, 1966 (in French).

[210] J. R. SHEWELL, *On the formation of quantum-mechanical operators*, Amer. J. Phys., 27 (1959), pp. 16–21.

[211] D. J. SIMMS, *Lie Groups and Quantum Mechanics*, Lecture Notes in Mathematics, No. 52, Springer-Verlag, Berlin, 1968.

[212] D. A. SMITH, *Chevalley bases for Lie modules*, Trans. Amer. Math. Soc., 115 (1965), pp. 283–299.

[213] ——, *A basis algorithm for finitely-generated Abelian groups*, Math. Algorithms, 1 (1966), pp. 14–35.

[214] J. M. SOURIAU, *Geometric Quantization*, Comm. Math. Phys., 1 (1966), pp. 374–398 (in French).

[215] B. SPAIN, *Tensor Calculus*, University Math. Texts, No. 17, Oliver and Boyd, London, 1956.

[216] D. R. SPEISER, *Fundamental representations of Lie groups*, Helv. Phys. Acta, 38 (1965), pp. 73–97.

[217] D. R. SPEISER AND J. TARSKI, *Possible schemes for global symmetry*, J. Mathematical Phys., 4 (1963), pp. 588–612.

[218] T. A. SPRINGER, *Weyl's character formula for algebraic groups*, Inventiones Math., 5 (1968), pp. 85–105.

[219] R. STEINBERG, *A general Clebsch–Gordan theorem*, Bull. Amer. Math. Soc., 67 (1961), pp. 401–407.

[220] E. L. STIEFEL, *An Introduction to Numerical Mathematics*, Academic Press, New York, 1963.

[221] N. STRAUMANN, *On the Clebsch–Gordan series of semisimple Lie algebras*, Helv. Phys. Acta, 38 (1965), pp. 56–64.

[222] ——, *Branching rules and Clebsch–Gordan series of semisimple Lie algebras*, Ibid., 38 (1965), pp. 481–498.

[223] R. F. STREATER, *Canonical quantization*, Comm. Math. Phys., 2 (1966), pp. 354–374.

[224] M. E. SWEEDLER, *Hopf Algebras*, W. A. Benjamin, New York, 1969.

[225] J. D. TALMAN, *Special Functions: A Group Theoretic Approach*, W. A. Benjamin, New York, 1968.

[226] J. TARSKI, *Partition function for certain simple Lie algebras*, J. Mathematical Phys., 4 (1963), pp. 569–574.

[227] U. UHLHORN, *Representation of symmetry transformations in quantum mechanics*, Ark. Fys., 23 (1963), pp. 307–340.

[228] B. L. VAN DER WAERDEN, *The classification of simple Lie groups*, Math. Z., 37 (1933), pp. 446–462.

[229] V. S. VARADARAJAN, *On the ring of invariant polynomials on a semisimple Lie algebra*, Amer. J. Math., 90 (1968), pp. 308–317.

[230] O. VEBLEN AND J. H. C. WHITEHEAD, *The Foundations of Differential Geometry*, Cambridge Tracts in Mathematics and Mathematical Physics, No. 29, Cambridge University Press, Cambridge, 1932.

[231] F. D. VELDKAMP, *Representations of algebraic groups of type F_4 in characteristic 2*, J. Algebra, 16 (1970), pp. 326–339.

[232] N. YA. VILENKIN, *On the theory of associated spherical functions*, Dokl. Akad. Nauk SSSR, 111 (1956), pp. 742–744 (in Russian).

[233] ——, *Bessel functions and representations of the group of Euclidean motions*, Uspekhi Mat. Nauk, 11 (1965), pp. 69–112 (in Russian).

[234] ——, *Special Functions and the Theory of Group Representations*, Amer. Math. Soc. Mathematical Monograph Translations, No. 22, Amer. Math. Soc., Providence, R.I., 1968.

[235] J. VON NEUMANN, *The uniqueness of the Schrödinger operators*, Ann. Math. Pura Appl., 104 (1931), pp. 570–578 (in German).

[236] J. WEI, *Note on the global validity of the Baker–Hausdorff and Magnus theorems*, J. Mathematical Phys., 4 (1963), pp. 1337–1341.

[237] L. WEISNER, *Group-theoretic origin of certain generating functions*, Pacific J. Math., 5 (1955), pp. 1033–1039.

[238] H. WEYL, *The Concept of a Riemann Surface*, first ed., B. G. Teubner, Leipzig, 1913 (in German).

[239] H. WEYL, *Theory of representations of continuous semisimple groups by linear transforma-tions. I*, Math. Z., 23 (1925), pp. 271–309.

[240] ———, *Theory of representations of continuous semisimple groups by linear transforma-tions. II*, Ibid., 24 (1926), pp. 328–376.

[241] ———, *Theory of representations of continuous semisimple groups by linear transforma-tions. III*, Ibid., 24 (1926), pp. 377–395.

[242] ———, *Theory of representations of continuous semisimple groups by linear transforma-tions. IV*, Ibid., 24 (1926), pp. 789–791.

[243] ———, *Harmonics on homogeneous manifolds*, Ann. of Math. (2), 35 (1934), pp. 486–499.

[244] ———, *The Classical Groups: Their Invariants and Representations*, 2nd ed., Princeton University Press, Princeton, N.J., 1946.

[245] J. H. C. WHITEHEAD, *On the decomposition of an infinitesimal group*, Proc. Cambridge Philos. Soc., 32 (1936), pp. 229–237.

[246] E. WICHMANN, *Note on the algebraic aspect of the integration of a system of ordinary linear differential equations*, J. Mathematical Phys., 2 (1961), pp. 876–880.

[247] E. P. WIGNER, *On the consequences of the symmetry of the nuclear Hamiltonian on the spectroscopy of nuclei*, Phys. Rev., 51 (1937), pp. 106–119.

[248] ———, *The application of group theory to the special functions of mathematical physics*, Princeton University Lecture Notes, Princeton, N.J., 1955, unpublished.

[249] ———, *Group Theory and its Application to the Quantum Mechanics of Atomic Spectra*, Vieweg and Son, Brunswick, Germany, 1931 (in German); English transl., Academic Press, New York, 1959.

[250] L. S. WOLLENBERG, *Sine and Poisson brackets—a distinction*, J. London Math. Soc., 44 (1969), pp. 592–594.

[251] ———, *Derivations of the Lie algebra of polynomials under Poisson bracket*, Proc. Amer. Math. Soc., 20 (1969), pp. 315–320.

[252] B. G. WYBOURNE, *Spectroscopic Properties of Rare Earths*, John Wiley, New York, 1965.

[253] C. N. YANG, *Elementary Particles: A Short History of Some Discoveries in Atomic Physics*, Princeton University Press, Princeton, N.J., 1961.

[254] G. ZAMBOTTI, *Factorization of differential equations and O(4) symmetry of the hydrogen atom*, Nuovo Cimento Suppl., 5 (1967), pp. 954–962.

INDEX